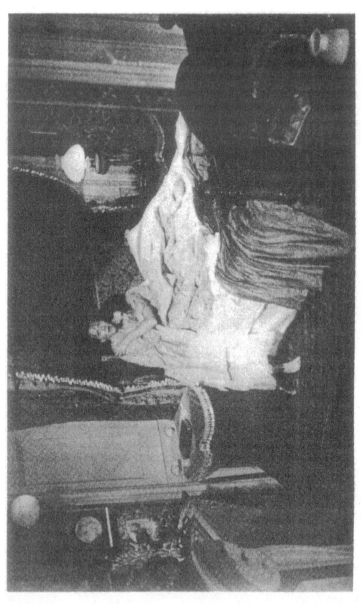

A scene from the Robert Wise production of THE HAUNTING released by Metro-Goldwyn-Mayer Inc.

THE HAUNTING OF HILL HOUSE

ADAPTED FOR THE STAGE BY
F. ANDREW LESLIE
FROM THE NOVEL BY
SHIRLEY JACKSON

★

DRAMATISTS
PLAY SERVICE
INC.

2

CAST OF CHARACTERS

In Order of Appearance:

ELEANOR VANCE

MRS. DUDLEY

THEODORA

DR. MONTAGUE

LUKE SANDERSON

MRS. MONTAGUE

ARTHUR PARKER

SYNOPSIS OF SCENES

ACT I

Act II

ACT III

The time is the present. The place is Hill House, a brooding, isolated and innately forbidding mansion located deep in the back country of an eastern State. The action is confined to a single set, which includes a windowless parlor and, at stage right, a small bedroom.

SPECIAL NOTE

Some groups may prefer to stage the play in two act rather than three act form. If so, this can readily be accomplished by placing the act break after the present Act II, scene 1 (which then becomes the final scene of the first act). The present Act II, scene 2 then becomes the first scene of the second act.

As the play is made up of six scenes overall, this means that the first three scenes will comprise Act I, and the last three scenes will become Act II, as opposed to the present arrangement of three acts with two scenes in each.

No other changes are required.

THE HAUNTING OF HILL HOUSE

ACT ONE

SCENE ONE

TIME: *Late afternoon, a day in early summer.*

PLACE: *Hill House, a brooding, isolated and innately forbidding mansion, located deep in the back country of an eastern State. The set is divided into two sections. The larger area, at L., represents an interior, windowless parlor or sitting room, while the smaller area, consisting of an angled platform at R., is a bedroom. There is a fireplace standing against the L. side of the platform about halfway up its length, but otherwise the separation between the two rooms is only suggested, although the bedroom is, obviously, in another part of the house.*

The furnishings in the parlor area include an ornate, curved-back sofa facing D.; two large chairs at L. of this with a table and lamp between them, and a small chess table with two straight chairs at D. R. Behind the sofa is a long table on which stands a large lamp with a stained-glass shade. There are also a desk and chair against the wall at U. L., and, at U. R., a sideboard with a wine decanter and glasses on it. Above the chess table, D. R., is an old-fashioned, tasseled standing lamp. At U. C. are double doors leading to an interior hall and, in the L. wall, a smaller, single door set above two steps. This door, as will be discovered later, leads to a stone tower. Both the mood and decor of the room are dark and chill.

The bedroom, which is approximately half the size of the parlor, is sparsely furnished, with a single bed and a

5

*bureau. The decor of this room is blue. There is a door
to the hallway at* U. C., *and a second door, connecting
with the adjoining bedroom, at* D. R. *Again no windows
are shown or suggested.*

*In both rooms the furniture and other items of stage dress-
ing should be heavy and cheerless, in a massive, dark and
essentially ugly mid-Victorian manner.*

*As the curtain rises the stage is empty and only the parlor
area is illuminated. After a moment the double doors at*
U. C. *open and Eleanor Vance enters, followed by Mrs.
Dudley. Eleanor is a plain-looking, conservatively dressed
girl in her late twenties. Mrs. Dudley, the housekeeper, is
a stern, uncommunicative woman of sixty or so, who
wears a dark housedress and a clean but faded apron.
Eleanor steps into the room and looks about in frank
curiosity, while Mrs. Dudley stands by the doors, her
hands folded in front of her.*

ELEANOR. (*Turning to Mrs. Dudley.*) I gather I'm the first one
here. (*Mrs. Dudley nods.*) Will there be many others? The doctor
didn't say in his letter. (*Mrs. Dudley shrugs.*) You did say you
were Mrs. Dudley?

MRS. DUDLEY. (*Sharply.*) I didn't say. But I am. (*Impatient.*)
Do you want to go to your room or wait here? You'll be in the
Blue room.

ELEANOR. (*Slightly put off by Mrs. Dudley's coldness.*) How
nice. (*Mrs. Dudley glowers.*) I mean . . . how nice to have blue.
It's always been my favorite color. (*She manages a tentative smile.*)

MRS. DUDLEY. Well?

ELEANOR. I think I'll wait here, if you don't mind.

MRS. DUDLEY. Suit yourself. Blue room's the first one on the
right—top of the stairs.

ELEANOR. I'll find it. Thank you. (*She turns away.*)

MRS. DUDLEY. (*Still in the doorway.*) I set dinner on the dining room sideboard at six sharp. You can serve yourselves. I clear
up in the morning. I have breakfast ready for you at nine. That's
the way I agreed to do. I can't keep the rooms up the way you'd
like, but there's no one else you could get that would help me. I
don't wait on people. What I agreed to, it doesn't mean I wait on
people.

6

ELEANOR. (*Not knowing quite what to make of this outpouring.*) Of course.

MRS. DUDLEY. I don't stay after I set out dinner. Not after it begins to get dark. (*Ominously.*) I leave before dark comes.

ELEANOR. I know. Dr. Montague mentioned in his letter . . .

MRS. DUDLEY. (*Breaking in.*) We live over in the town, six miles away.

ELEANOR. Yes.

MRS. DUDLEY. (*Going on.*) So there won't be anyone around if you need help.

ELEANOR. I understand.

MRS. DUDLEY. We couldn't even hear you, in the night.

ELEANOR. I don't suppose . . .

MRS. DUDLEY. No one could. No one lives any nearer than the town. No one else will come any nearer than that.

ELEANOR. (*Resigned.*) I know.

MRS. DUDLEY. (*A little smile on her lips.*) In the night . . . In the dark. (*They look at each other in silence for a moment. Then Eleanor turns away, somewhat unsettled by Mrs. Dudley's recital. From off* L. *comes the ring of the doorbell.*) Someone else is here. I'll go now.

ELEANOR. (*Turning back.*) Mrs. Dudley . . . (*But Mrs. Dudley has gone, leaving the doors open behind her. After a moment Eleanor resumes her study of the room, and then crosses to the small door at* L. *She tries to open it, but it is locked. She turns and moves slowly back towards* R., *stopping to examine the ornate chess set at* D. C. *As she is looking at one of the pieces the double doors close slowly with a click. She turns sharply at the sound.*) Mrs. Dudley? (*There is no answer. Eleanor frowns and shivers slightly, then puts the chess piece down, and crosses to one of the chairs at* D. L. *She sits, picking up a book from the small table between the chairs. While she thumbs through it she continues to look about the room, as though trying to fathom its special personality. Then the doors are opened again and Theodora enters, followed by Mrs. Dudley—who remains in the doorway as before. Theodora is about the same age as Eleanor, but dark and rather exotic looking. A creature of mood and sudden impulse. Eleanor puts her book down and jumps up to greet her.*) Thank heaven someone else has come. (*Then, suddenly embarrassed by her bold-*

7

ness.) I mean . . . I was beginning to feel sort of . . . remote
. . . here. (*She extends her hand.*) I'm Eleanor Vance.

THEODORA. (*Grasping Eleanor's hand.*) How do you do. And
please don't apologize. This *bloody* house. Two minutes and already it's given me the cold chills. I'm Theodora. Just Theodora.

ELEANOR. (*With attempted lightness.*) Welcome to Hill House.
I'd guess that this used to be the embalming room. I hate to think
what it's like upstairs.

THEODORA. (*Facetiously.*) It's the home I've always dreamed
of . . . a little hideaway where I can be alone with my thoughts
—particularly if they happen to be about murder or suicide or—

MRS. DUDLEY. (*Breaking in sharply.*) You'll be in the Green
room.

THEODORA. (*Turning.*) Oh?

MRS. DUDLEY. Do you want to go up now or wait here?

THEODORA. Since you put it so graciously, I think I'll stay here
for awhile. If Eleanor doesn't object.

MRS. DUDLEY. Suit yourself. But I'd get settled before dark if
I were you. I leave then, so there won't be anyone around if you
need help. (*She turns and goes before either of the others can com-
ment. Theodora looks after her for a moment.*)

THEODORA. (*Turning back to Eleanor.*) Charming soul.

ELEANOR. (*Absently.*) She walks without making a sound.

THEODORA. (*Questioning.*) What?

ELEANOR. It's nothing . . . just that it's so utterly quiet here.
As though the house *wanted* silence—and she was afraid not to
obey.

THEODORA. Afraid? Dear girl, how long have you been here?

ELEANOR. (*Her mood still uncertain.*) Not long, really. I came
just before you did. But that's another thing. *Time* seems alien
here, too.

THEODORA. (*Lightly.*) You're probably just hungry. I'm starved
myself, and *nothing* unsettles me more than that. I snap and snarl
and imagine all sorts of things.

ELEANOR. (*Brightening.*) Maybe you're right. It does seem a
long time since I stopped for lunch. I hope Mrs. Dudley's a good
cook. Did she give a full recital of what she does here?

THEODORA. (*Crossing L. to sit.*) Oh, yes. (*Imitating Mrs. Dudley.*) "I don't wait on people. What I agreed to, it doesn't mean
I wait on people."

8

ELEANOR. (*With a laugh.*) And she won't come if we scream in the night.

THEODORA. It was not what she agreed to.

ELEANOR. But I'd rather not be *all* alone, either. I hope our rooms are near.

THEODORA. They connect. Laughing girl told me. (*Eleanor has seated herself on the sofa. The doors click shut again. Eleanor looks quickly over her shoulder.*)

ELEANOR. They did it again.

THEODORA. What did what again?

ELEANOR. The doors—closing by themselves.

THEODORA. (*Tucking her legs up under her.*) Oh? (*Teasing Eleanor.*) Maybe the house *wants* them to close.

ELEANOR. But it happened before.

THEODORA. Of course it did. Poor baby. You *are* starving. Now tell me about yourself—and the mysterious Dr. Montague. I presume you're here because of his invitation.

ELEANOR. (*Turning back to Theodora.*) I am, but he's a mystery to me, too. All I know is that he wrote to me that he was interested in the analysis of supernatural manifestations, and that he had taken Hill House for the summer. It has a reputation for . . . I think he called it "psychic activity."

THEODORA. He didn't actually come out and call it haunted?

ELEANOR. Not in so many words. But he did say that he thought it would be helpful to have others present who were . . . well, sensitive to abnormal disturbances. Actually he was very scientific about it, being a professor and all that. I suppose he thought we might find it interesting too.

THEODORA. Do you think we will?

ELEANOR. (*Doubtfully.*) I don't know. It's not the sort of thing one dreams and plans about. My experience with psychic activity is hardly extensive. There was just that one time—and I was only a child. (*Theodora looks at her questioningly.*)

THEODORA. Can you tell me about it?

ELEANOR. Of course. It was just after my father died. I was twelve and my sister was eighteen. One day showers of stones began to fall on the house—not on any other house on the block, but just on ours. Mother said that the neighbors had caused it, because they never liked us and didn't want us on the block. People came from all over to watch, and the stones kept falling on and off for three days—dropping from the ceiling, rolling down the walls, breaking windows, pattering on the roof. It was the strangest thing I'd ever seen. Then my sister and I went to stay with a friend—and the stones stopped. They never came back again, but there was quite a lot of publicity about it, and I suppose that Dr. Montague remembered.

THEODORA. Do you still live in the house?

ELEANOR. I left after Mother died. (*With deliberate lightness.*) Now I have a cozy little place of my own in the city. It's bright and snug. Not dark and cold like this awful house.

THEODORA. (*Lightly.*) You seemed willing enough to come.

ELEANOR. (*Casually.*) Why not? I had the time free and it did sound sort of intriguing—and different. Besides, my brother-in-law checked up on Dr. Montague to make sure it was all O.K. (*Changing the direction of conversation.*) But what about you? You're here, too.

THEODORA. (*Shrugging.*) I guess I was as curious as you were —and perhaps a little flattered at being asked. Also, I had a spat with my roommate and wanted to be somewhere else for awhile. (*She looks around the room.*) Now I'm not so sure.

ELEANOR. (*Questioningly.*) Did something happen to you, too? I mean to make Dr. Montague invite you?

THEODORA. (*Lightly.*) Oh Lord, I'm famous. I'm the girl who can identify nineteen cards out of twenty every time. When they're held up out of sight. They call it extra sensory perception, and I'm loaded with it. If the house *is* haunted I should be the first one to know about it. Still— I don't think I ever imagined that there really *would* be something like a Hill House. Reading cards without seeing them is one thing . . . coming here is another. Somehow you don't expect places like this to actually exist.

ELEANOR. (*Teasing.*) But some of us go around hoping.

THEODORA. (*With a laugh.*) Well anyway, we're fellow babes in the woods. So let's get settled—*and* stick together. (*She rises.*) Do you think we should check in with Mrs. Dudley, or just go up to our rooms?

ELEANOR. (*Shrugging.*) She probably watches every move we make, anyway. Part of what she agreed to.

THEODORA. Agreed to with whom, I wonder. Count Dracula?

ELEANOR. (*Playing the game.*) You think *he* lives in Hill House?

THEODORA. I think he spends all his weekends here. I swear I saw bats in the woodwork out there. (*She gestures towards the hall.*) Come on, let's go and see what horror awaits upstairs.

ELEANOR. All right. (*She rises.*) Incidentally, did you notice that door? (*She points* L.) I tried to open it before you came. It's locked.

THEODORA. (*Intrigued.*) Oh? (*She crosses* L. *to the door.*) Let's explore. Maybe we'll find the secret of Hill House—or the place where Dr. Montague conducts his weird experiments. (*She reaches the door and tries the handle. It is locked. Eleanor crosses to behind her. She tries to peer through the keyhole. She pulls back. Then, in a low voice.*) Dark as night. Dark as those black hills that surround Hill House. (*She turns to Eleanor.*) Did you notice them? It seemed as though they wanted to fall on me when I arrived.

ELEANOR. (*Quietly.*) They won't fall on you. They'll just slide down, silently and secretly, rolling over you if you try to run away.

THEODORA. (*With feigned annoyance.*) Thank you. What Mrs. Dudley has started you have completed nicely. I shall pack and go home at once.

ELEANOR. (*Suddenly serious.*) Please don't say that. I couldn't stay here alone. Not now.

THEODORA. (*Sensing her fear.*) Poor Eleanor. I was only teasing. (*She touches Eleanor's cheek.*) I think you're afraid. I think you've been afraid all the time, ever since I came into this room. (*Eleanor turns away.*) You mustn't be afraid all the time. We'll be all right, together. (*Eleanor looks away, ashamed and flustered. The* U. C. *doors open silently during this, and Mrs. Dudley appears. She watches for a moment before speaking.*)

MRS. DUDLEY. You'd better come now. (*Eleanor and Theodora turn to her.*) I'll show you your rooms. I set dinner on the sideboard at six o'clock sharp and then I go. I don't stay around after that.

THEODORA. (*Archly.*) Not when it's dark.

MRS. DUDLEY. That's right. I'm gone before it's dark.

ELEANOR. (*Her light mood restored.*) So you won't hear us if we scream in the night. (*She glances at Theodora conspiratorially.*)

MRS. DUDLEY. (*Her face set.*) Nobody will. You'll see. Nobody will hear you. (*Eleanor and Theodora exchange glances.*) We'd

11

better go now. (*She stands aside and waits. Eleanor and Theodora pause a moment.*)

THEODORA. (*Gesturing for Eleanor to precede her.*) Shall we? It might be nice to freshen up before dinner. Maybe we'll have time for a walk.

ELEANOR. (*Motioning her ahead.*) After you. I insist.

THEODORA. (*With a wry face.*) Hmm. Thanks a lot. (*She strides towards the door.*) Spirits—watch out. Theodora is coming.

ELEANOR. (*Following after her.*) And Eleanor, her long-lost cousin Eleanor.

THEODORA. (*Pausing at the door.*) Yes, of course. Maybe we *are* cousins. And long-lost.

ELEANOR. But we'll never be separated again.

THEODORA. Or afraid. Right?

ELEANOR. (*Motioning her ahead.*) Of course. What's there to be afraid of? (*They go out. Mrs. Dudley follows impassively, leaving the door open behind her. The stage is empty for a moment as we hear them going off. Then the doors shut slowly, and there is silence. The lights dim briefly to denote the passage of time, and then come up again a few moments later. The doors open and Dr. Montague enters, followed by Luke Sanderson. Dr. Montague is roly-poly and bearded, with steel-rimmed glasses and a distinctly professional air. Luke, in his early thirties, has good looks and the disturbing charm of a man with a well-educated but usually empty mind.*)

DR. MONTAGUE. (*Holding the door open for Luke.*) Ah, here we are. The small parlor. (*Luke stops in the doorway.*) Come in, my boy, come in. It's much the most pleasant room in the house, believe me.

LUKE. (*Stepping in, with a wry face.*) I think you mean it.

DR. MONTAGUE. (*Rubbing his hands together.*) I do, I do. I can tell you I've seen far worse in my work.

LUKE. That's reassuring. (*He looks about the room.*) There'll be others coming, I trust.

DR. MONTAGUE. They're here. Two charming ladies. Mrs. Dudley informed me that they've gone out to explore the grounds.

LUKE. Alone?

DR. MONTAGUE. Of course. My dear boy, I don't know what your aunt has told you about Hill House. But there is no physical danger to any of us.

LUKE. Have you explained this to Mrs. Dudley?

DR. MONTAGUE. (*Amused.*) I would venture to guess that no one explains anything to Mrs. Dudley. Not even *Mr.* Dudley. But let's not give rein to our imaginations. Our interest is scientific, and I am more pleased than I can say to think that we are all here safely and on time—with the fascinating secrets of Hill House awaiting our investigation.

LUKE. (*Settling into one of* D. L. *chairs.*) Like a package under the Christmas tree.

DR. MONTAGUE. If you will. (*There is a noise off* U. C. *Dr. Montague holds up his hand for silence.*) I believe the ladies have returned. If you'll pardon me. (*He crosses* U. *and opens the doors.*) This way, ladies. Can you hear my voice?

THEODORA. (*Off.*) Is there a light? It's black as pitch out here.

DR. MONTAGUE. (*Peering into the hall.*) You're doing fine. Open the door directly ahead of you. That's it. (*Pause. He steps aside to admit Theodora and Eleanor.*) Ladies, welcome. Come inside. I am Dr. Montague. (*They enter. Eleanor now wears a red sweater and Theodora a yellow one. Theodora comes in first.*)

THEODORA. (*Shaking his hand.*) Theodora.

DR. MONTAGUE. Of course, welcome to Hill House. (*He turns to Eleanor.*) And you are Miss Vance. (*Eleanor nods.*) So glad that you both could come. And this is Luke Sanderson. Miss Vance and Miss . . .

THEODORA. Just Theodora. Last names mean so little.

LUKE. (*Rising.*) How true. (*Bowing to them both.*) My pleasure.

ELEANOR. (*Suddenly.*) But your last name means something. At least here. You're one of the family, aren't you? I mean, Hill House is yours.

LUKE. (*Lightly.*) I can't deny it. At present my aunt holds title, but someday this stately pile will probably belong to me—worse luck. Until then, however, I am here as one of Dr. Montague's guests. My first visit, I might add—so this is all new to me, too.

DR. MONTAGUE. (*Explaining.*) Mrs. Sanderson, Luke's aunt, agreed to allow me a short lease to carry out my research on condition that a member of the family be one of my party. We're fortunate that Luke was able to fulfill her request.

LUKE. They hope I'll dissuade him from digging up the lovely old scandals.

THEODORA. Scandals? Were there really?

13

DR. MONTAGUE. Indeed there were. We'll get to all that in due time. Now perhaps a bit of sherry would be appealing. Before we go in to dinner. (*To Luke.*) Luke, my boy, would you do the honors?

LUKE. (*Crossing u. to the sideboard.*) Delighted.

ELEANOR. (*Quickly.*) I could use something. I'm still a bit shaky after that . . . rabbit.

THEODORA. (*Lightly.*) We, you see, are two little girls who were planning a picnic down by the brook and got scared home by a rabbit. (*Dr. Montague reacts.*)

LUKE. (*At the sideboard.*) I go in mortal fear of rabbits, myself.

ELEANOR. (*Quietly.*) If that's what it was.

DR. MONTAGUE. (*To Eleanor.*) What else do you think it might have been?

ELEANOR. I don't know. We were sitting by the brook, and I felt as though someone or something was watching us. On the hill, across the brook. Then it moved—but I couldn't see anything—only the grass bending.

THEODORA. It was a rabbit. What else?

DR. MONTAGUE. (*Musing.*) Exactly. What else? (*Luke crosses D. with a tray of filled sherry glasses and a decanter. He serves the ladies first. Dr. Montague takes his glass in turn.*) Ah. Thank you. (*He raises his glass.*) Again, welcome to Hill House—and to our success here. (*They all drink.*)

LUKE. (*Curiously.*) How would one reckon success, exactly, in a situation like this?

DR. MONTAGUE. (*Pleasantly.*) Let's just say that I hope all of us will have an exciting visit and that the book which I shall write about our findings will rock my colleagues back on their heels.

THEODORA. Hear, hear. (*Luke raises his glass in agreement. Eleanor smiles at them both.*)

DR. MONTAGUE. You see, your visit here will be something more than a vacation. I'm hopeful of your working, or at least helping me to attain as thorough an understanding as possible of all that might happen while we're here.

ELEANOR. How, doctor?

DR. MONTAGUE. With notes. Notes on everything you see, or hear, or feel. As complete and detailed as you can manage. It shouldn't prove an unbearable task.

THEODORA. (*Holding her empty glass out to Luke.*) So long as

no one makes any puns about mixing spirits and spirits. May I?
(*Luke crosses to her and refills her glass.*)

DR. MONTAGUE. (*Peering at her.*) Spirits? Oh, of course. (*He laughs.*) Spirits, indeed.

ELEANOR. Everything's so strange. I mean, this morning I was wondering what Hill House would be like, and now I can't believe that it's all quite real, and we're here.

LUKE. (*Offering more sherry to Eleanor.*) Since we are all here, shouldn't we get better acquainted? We only know names so far. For example, I know that it is Eleanor, here, who is wearing the red sweater, so, consequently it must be you, Theodora, (*He turns towards Theodora.*) who wears yellow.

THEODORA. (*Going along with him.*) Doctor Montague has a beard—so you must be Luke.

ELEANOR. (*To Theodora.*) And you are Theodora, because I am Eleanor.

LUKE. I have no beard, so he (*Pointing to Dr. Montague.*) must be Dr. Montague.

DR. MONTAGUE. (*Amused.*) Exactly. And I have a beard because my wife likes them. (*They laugh. Dr. Montague holds his glass out to Luke.*)

LUKE. (*Filling Dr. Montague's glass.*) Well, then, now that I know which of us is me let me identify myself further. I am, in private life, let me see . . . a bullfighter.

ELEANOR. (*Lightly.*) And I am an artist's model. I live a mad, abandoned life, draped in a shawl and going from garret to garret.

LUKE. Are you heartless and wanton?

THEODORA. Are you losing your beauty, and coughing a good deal?

ELEANOR. (*Reflectively.*) I rather think I have a heart of gold. At any rate my affairs are the talk of the cafes.

THEODORA. (*Loftily.*) And I am the daughter of the lord of the manor. Ordinarily I go clad in silk and lace, but I've borrowed my maid's finery to appear among you. I may of course become so enamored of the common life that I will never go back—and the poor girl will have to get herself new clothes. And you, Dr. Montague?

DR. MONTAGUE. (*Smiling.*) A pilgrim. A wanderer.

LUKE. Truly a congenial little group. Hill House has surely never seen our like.

THEODORA. I'll give the honor to Hill House. I've never seen its like. (*She glances about the room.*) This room, for example. What on earth do they call it?

DR. MONTAGUE. A parlor, perhaps. I considered that we might be more comfortable here than in one of the other rooms. It's well located to serve as a sort of center of operations. It may not be cheerful . . .

THEODORA. (*Breaking in.*) Of *course* it's cheerful. There is nothing more exhilarating than maroon upholstery and oak paneling, and what is that over there, (*She gestures towards the small door at* L.) the door to the snake pit?

DR. MONTAGUE. Tomorrow you will see it all for yourselves. We'll explore the entire house. (*Turning.*) As for that door—it leads into the stone tower, which you might have noticed as you came up the drive.

ELEANOR. (*Surprised.*) But that was at the far corner of the house. Here we're in the middle, without even a window.

DR. MONTAGUE. (*Smiling.*) So it seems. Let's just say that the house has its little oddities. I've studied a map of it, and I still can't quite explain the reasoning to you. For example, when we go in to dinner, which the now departed Mrs. Dudley has spread for us, we go through the doors there, (*He gestures* U. C.) down the passage, i...o the front hall, and then across the hall and through the billiard room and into the dining room. Roundabout, isn't it? But I'm sure you'll find it easy with practice.

THEODORA. Someone is going to have to lead me. I'd starve if I had to find it on my own.

ELEANOr. But why so many little rooms?

LUKE. Maybe they liked to hide from each other.

THEODORA. That does explain why everything is so dark.

DR. MONTAGUE. Some of the rooms *are* entirely inside rooms, and therefore poorly lighted. However, a series of closed rooms is not altogether surprising in a house of this period. But tomorrow . . .

THEODORA. (*Concerned.*) We ought to make a practice of leaving the doors open.

ELEANOR. You'd have to prop them with something, then. Every door in this house swings shut when you let go of it.

DR. MONTAGUE. I'll make our first note. Door stops—lots of them. (*He rises.*) Now, shall we see about dinner?

16

THEODORA. Do you think we should? I mean when I look at this house, and then remember our dear Mrs. Dudley.

ELEANOR. Yes, what keeps *her* here?

THEODORA. *And* her husband. If that spectre I saw at the gate was Mr. Dudley.

DR. MONTAGUE. As I understand it, the Dudleys have taken care of Hill House as long as anyone can remember. The arrangement seems to be satisfactory to all concerned.

THEODORA. Maybe she and Dudley hoard their gold in a secret chamber—or there's oil under the house.

DR. MONTAGUE. (*Flatly.*) There are no secret chambers in Hill House. The possibility has been suggested, of course, but I think I may say with assurance that no such romantic devices exist here. But tomorrow . . .

LUKE. In any case, oil is definitely old hat. Nowadays it's uranium. Perhaps the Dudleys plan to murder me in cold blood for the uranium.

THEODORA. Or just for the pure fun of it.

ELEANOR. (*Suddenly quite serious.*) Yes, but why are *we* here?

THEODORA. (*After a moment of silence.*) Just what I was going to ask. Why *are* we here? What *is* wrong with Hill House? What is going to happen?

DR. MONTAGUE. Tomorrow—

THEODORA. (*Firmly.*) No. We are three adult, intelligent people, Doctor, and we have all come a long way to meet you here at Hill House. We want to know why.

LUKE. I second the motion.

ELEANOR. Why *did* you ask us to come, Doctor? How did you know about Hill House, and why does it have such a reputation, and what really goes on here?

DR. MONTAGUE. (*Quietly.*) Actually, I know less than I might wish about Hill House, except by reputation, although I intended to tell you everything I *do* know. As for what is going to happen, I will learn that when you do. But tomorrow is soon enough to talk about it, I think.

THEODORA. Not for me. Not if I'm going to get any sleep.

DR. MONTAGUE. I assure you that Hill House will be quiet tonight. There is a pattern in these things.

LUKE. I really think we ought to talk it over now.

ELEANOR. We're not afraid.

17

DR. MONTAGUE. (*Sighing.*) Suppose you heard the story of Hill House and decided not to stay. How would you leave, tonight? Hill House has a reputation for insistent hospitality. The last person who tried to leave in darkness—it was eighteen years ago, I grant you—was killed at the turn in the driveway. His horse bolted and crushed him against the big tree.

THEODORA. But we're not going to run away. (*She turns to the others.*) Are we? (*Eleanor nods.*)

LUKE. Stoutly, upon the ramparts.

DR. MONTAGUE. (*Shaking his head.*) You are a mutinous group of assistants. (*He sits down again.*) All right, I'll be as brief as I can. (*He muses for a moment. The others watch him in silence.*) To be frank, I didn't know just how best to prepare the three of you for Hill House. I couldn't put it all in a letter, and even now I'm reluctant to influence your minds with its complete history before you've had a chance to see all of the house for yourselves. To talk about it this way could be . . . misleading.

THEODORA. Don't give it a thought, Doctor. I'm sure we're all in the mood for a ghost story.

DR. MONTAGUE. (*Frowning.*) That's hardly what I have in mind. We're not children trying to frighten one another.

THEODORA. (*Smiling.*) Sorry. Just trying to get myself used to all of this.

DR. MONTAGUE. (*Seriously.*) We must exercise great caution in our language. Preconceived notions of ghosts and apparitions . . .

LUKE. (*Breaking in.*) The disembodied hand in the soup. (*The girls laugh.*)

DR. MONTAGUE. (*Turning to Luke.*) My dear boy. If you please. What I want to say is that our purpose here is scientific and exploratory. We cannot let it be affected, or even warped, by spooky stories which would be better told around a campfire. We're here to test certain theories regarding psychic phenomena. As a matter of fact, it would be better if you knew nothing about Hill House. Ideally you should be ignorant and receptive.

THEODORA. (*In a low voice.*) And take notes.

DR. MONTAGUE. (*Agreeably.*) And take notes, yes. However, since you press me, let me put it this way. There is a concept that certain houses are unclean or forbidden—just as others, like churches, for example, have atmospheres of holiness and goodness. Perhaps you could say that some houses are born bad. Hill House, whatever the cause, has been unfit for human habitation for some twenty years. What it was like before then, whether its personality was molded by the people who lived here, or the things they did, or whether it was evil from its start, I do not know. I hope, however, that some of these questions will be answered before we leave. But no one knows, even, why some houses are called haunted.

LUKE. What else *could* you call Hill House?

DR. MONTAGUE. Disturbed, perhaps. Or sick. Or leprous. Although haunted will do. And yet there are always those who are ready to discount the eerie, or mysterious. What I call psychic disturbances they will ascribe to subterranean waters, or electric currents, or polluted air, or even sun spots. Anything to bring it all out in the open and give a clear explanation to it. But, you see, sometimes it isn't so easily done. I've checked with every tenant who has tried to live in Hill House. They've all left hastily—but every one has tried to give a natural reason for doing so. The dampness, pressing business elsewhere, and so forth. And yet, when I questioned them further, they were unwilling to talk about it. But they all agreed on one point. They urged me to stay as far away from Hill House as possible. They thought it should be burned down, and its secrets with it.

ELEANOR. Then there *was* a scandal.

DR. MONTAGUE. Very definitely. With suicide, madness and lawsuits.

LUKE. (*Dourly.*) It's harder to burn down a house than you think.

DR. MONTAGUE. But the *truth* of the House, its reason for being haunted, for want of a better term, remains to be probed. That is why I am here, and why I invited you to join me. You, Theodora, because of your telepathic ability, and you, Eleanor, because of your involvement in poltergeist phenomena. Perhaps together we can induce the power of Hill House to reveal itself.

ELEANOR. (*Uncertainly.*) But that was so long ago. I hardly remember.

THEODORA. (*Ignoring her.*) But *why*, Doctor? I mean, I can accept that Hill House is supposed to be haunted, and you want us to keep track of what happens. But what's here? What frightens people so?

DR. MONTAGUE. I will not put a name to what has no name. I don't know. But perhaps before we leave . . .

19

ELEANOR. (*Still preoccupied with her own thoughts.*) I never really knew what was going on. My mother said it was the neighbors.

LUKE. (*Slowly.*) I think that all we want is facts. Something we can understand and put together.

DR. MONTAGUE. Exactly. But the first question is this. Do you want to leave? Now, before you become more deeply involved? (*He looks at Eleanor.*)

ELEANOR. (*Sheepishly.*) No. And I'm sorry about this afternoon. The rabbit, I mean. I shouldn't have let myself get so frightened.

THEODORA. (*Loyally.*) Nonsense. You were no more frightened than I was. We were both scared to death.

LUKE. Horrible creatures, rabbits.

DR. MONTAGUE. (*Pleasantly.*) I think we all had cause for nervousness. Just turning the corner and seeing Hill House for the first time was a rude shock.

LUKE. I thought he was going to send the car into a tree.

ELEANOR. (*Thoughtfully.*) I don't think we could leave now if we wanted to. (*There is something in her tone of voice which makes the others turn towards her. She is flustered, and adds lamely.*) Mrs. Dudley would never forgive us.

DR. MONTAGUE. (*With a polite laugh.*) Of course. But to go on. Hill House was built some eighty years ago, by a man named Hugh Crain. It was meant as a country home for his family, and was quite luxurious by the standards of its time. From the beginning it was a sad house. Hugh Crain's young wife died minutes before she was to set her eyes on the house for the first time. Her carriage overturned in the driveway. She was crushed to death. Hugh Crain was a sad and bitter man—but he had two small daughters to bring up, so he did not leave Hill House.

ELEANOR. (*Incredulously.*) Children grew up here?

DR. MONTAGUE. Why not? The climate is quite good, actually. And there is no dampness, despite the rumors. Lonely, perhaps, but not an unhealthy place on the face of it.

THEODORA. Poor little things.

DR. MONTAGUE. Their father married again. Twice more, as a matter of fact. The second Mrs. Crain died of a fall. The third of consumption, at a European health resort. Crain had left the two little girls here in the care of a governess, but after his third wife died he closed the house, remained abroad, and sent his daughters to live with a cousin of their mother's.

THEODORA. I hope their life was jollier after that. It's not good to think of children growing up like mushrooms, in this dark place.

DR. MONTAGUE. To be honest the two sisters never got along too well, and after their father died and left Hill House to them jointly, the bickering over it went on until the younger sister married.

ELEANOR. Stole her sister's beau, no doubt.

DR. MONTAGUE. (*Agreeably.*) Perhaps so. At any rate it was said that the older sister was crossed in love. She came back here to live, alone at first, until she found a village girl to stay with her as housekeeper and companion. Then the younger sister began to make trouble again. She said that she had assigned her share in Hill House to her sister on the condition that she be given certain heirlooms—which she claimed she never received. A set of gold-rimmed dishes was one bone of contention.

THEODORA. I don't like the younger sister. First she stole her sister's lover, and then she went after her dishes, too.

DR. MONTAGUE. Things got worse, unfortunately. When the older sister died the companion insisted that Hill House had been left to her, but the younger sister and her husband went to court trying to prove that the older sister had been tricked into signing away her property. There was even a suggestion of murder. They lost their case, but they never stopped trying to get the house back, by any means. At one point the companion was forced to ask for police protection. People in the area sided with the younger sister, so the companion was not only bedeviled, but friendless. Eventually she killed herself.

ELEANOR. (*Shocked.*) Killed herself? She had to do that?

DR. MONTAGUE. You mean was there no other way of escaping her tormentors? Apparently she didn't think so, although local rumor had it that she chose suicide because her guilty conscience drove her to it. She was tenacious, but the constant, nagging persecution wore her down. She was also convinced that the younger sister came into the house at night to steal things—despite all the locks and bolts.

ELEANOR. She should have gone away. As far as she could go.

DR. MONTAGUE. In a sense she did. She hanged herself from the turret of the stone tower beyond that door. (*He nods* L.) After her death the house passed on to her cousins, the Sandersons. The sister gave them trouble, too, but always swore that she would not and had not come into the house at night—even to steal things.

LUKE. Was anything ever really stolen?

DR. MONTAGUE. Let's say that no proof was ever given. But the story of a nightly intruder did enhance the reputation of the house still further.

THEODORA. (*Sourly.*) Suicide, murder, burglary. A happy place, this.

DR. MONTAGUE. The sister died before long, but the Sandersons never did live in Hill House. They told people they planned to do so, and even spent a few days here. Then they cleared out, and no one has lived here since, except for a day or so at a time.

ELEANOR. (*Shaking her head.*) Those two poor little girls. I can't forget them, walking through these dark rooms, trying to play dolls, maybe, in here or in those awful bedrooms upstairs.

LUKE. (*Thoughtfully.*) And the old house has just been sitting here. Nothing in it touched, nothing used, nothing here wanted by anyone any more, just sitting here pondering the past.

ELEANOR. And waiting.

DR. MONTAGUE. (*Nodding his head.*) And waiting. (*In a serious tone.*) Essentially the evil is in the house itself, I think. It has enchained and destroyed its people and their lives; it is a place of contained ill will. (*He rises.*) Well, enough of that. To-morrow you shall see it all for yourselves. The Sandersons put in electricity and plumbing, but otherwise nothing has been changed. Now I suggest we repair to the dining room and find out what delights Mrs. Dudley has left for us. One *pleasant* rumor about this place is that she is a rather good cook. Let's hope so. (*He crosses* u. *towards the doors.*)

THEODORA. (*Getting up.*) It's probably bat stew.

ELEANOR. (*With a laugh.*) And cobweb pudding. (*She rises, and follows Theodora* u. *towards the doors.*)

DR. MONTAGUE. (*Turning at the doors.*) Oh yes, one other thing. It may seem incomprehensible to you now, but a place like this . . . sometimes it can begin to affect you without your really being aware. I don't mean the things that occur outwardly, but rather what might happen to you inwardly, as it were. I want you to promise me that if you feel the house "catching" at you you will

22

tell me—immediately. Our value here is as a team. A clear-headed and objective team.

THEODORA. (*With an appropriate gesture.*) I promise, scout's honor. I'm with you, and against this bloody house.

ELEANOR. I echo the sentiment. But all this talk has made me hungrier than I realized.

DR. MONTAGUE. (*Standing aside to let them pass, as Luke crosses u. to join him.*) We can do something about that. And if you will do as I ask we'll be able to settle some other questions, too, I'm sure. (*He motions Luke to go on out.*) After you, I insist.

LUKE. (*Nodding in thanks.*) Many thanks. And I wouldn't be concerned about your team, Doctor. I'm sure we'll all be very comfortable here. Productive, too. (*He goes out.*)

DR. MONTAGUE. (*Pulling the door closed as he exits after Luke.*) Of course, my boy, of course. Very comfortable indeed. Why shouldn't we be? (*There is silence for a moment, and then the lights are slowly dimmed as*)

THE CURTAIN FALLS

ACT ONE

SCENE TWO

That night. The parlor is dark, but the bedroom area, R., is dimly lighted by a lamp on the bureau. Eleanor, alone in the room, is finishing her unpacking. She is dressed in a nightgown and robe. She makes several trips to the bureau to put things away, then snaps her suitcase shut and slides it under the bed. She sits on the bed for a moment, studying the room, and then goes to the door at D. R. and taps on it.

ELEANOR. (*Softly.*) Theo? (*There is no answer. She taps again, more firmly.*) Theo? (*She frowns.*)

THEODORA'S VOICE. (*Beyond the door.*) I'll be right there. Open the door if you want to.

ELEANOR. (*Visibly relieved. She opens the door and peers beyond it.*) What were you doing? It was so quiet in there.

THEODORA. (*Entering the room. She too is dressed in night-gown and robe.*) I was doing my nails, silly. Did you think the goblins got me? (*She crosses to C. of the area, holding up her hands, with fingers spread.*) See—red. I love decorating myself. Someday I'll paint myself all over.

ELEANOR. (*Laughing.*) With gold paint, no doubt.

THEODORA. (*Loftily.*) Nail polish and perfume. And maybe mascara. Don't laugh. You should think more about such things yourself.

ELEANOR. No time.

THEODORA. (*Shaking her head.*) Poor Nell. I shall take you in hand and make a different person out of you. I don't like being with women of no color. (*Menacingly.*) Maybe I'll put red polish on your toes—right now.

ELEANOR. (*Backing away with a laugh.*) Oh no you won't! (*She sits on the bed.*)

THEODORA. (*Crossing towards her.*) Surely a famous courtesan like yourself is accustomed to the ministrations of hand-maidens. (*She holds her hand out expectantly. Eleanor curls her feet under her.*)

ELEANOR. I can't . . . I hate having things done to me.

THEODORA. (*Dropping her hand.*) Well, you're about as crazy as anyone I ever saw.

ELEANOR. (*Looking away.*) I don't like to feel helpless. My mother . . .

THEODORA. (*Breaking in.*) Your mother would have been delighted to see you with red toenails.

ELEANOR. (*Looking at Theodora.*) It's wicked. I mean on *my* feet. It would make me feel like a fool.

THEODORA. (*Sitting beside her.*) You've got foolishness and wickedness mixed up. (*Teasing.*) Just think how pleasantly surprised Dr. Montague and Luke would be.

ELEANOR. (*Pettishly.*) No matter what I say, you make it seem foolish.

THEODORA. (*Looking at Eleanor.*) Or wicked. (*Seriously.*) You know what I think, Nell? I think that you ought to go home. (*She gets up.*)

ELEANOR. (*Upset.*) I don't want to go. Why should I?

THEODORA. (*Turning to her. Quietly.*) Because you're still afraid. And you have been ever since we've been here.

24

ELEANOR. (*A note of desperation in her voice.*) No. I was an idiot this afternoon, about the rabbit. It was a surprise, that's all. It's only that I'm tired. I'm not used to driving as far as I did today. (*She looks anxiously at Theodora.*)

THEODORA. (*After a moment, with understanding.*) You do look pale. You should be in bed. I'll go to my room. (*She turns.*)

ELEANOR. (*Suddenly.*) Don't go, not yet. Couldn't we talk awhile? I think I'm too restless to sleep right away.

THEODORA. (*Smiling.*) Of course. (*She crosses back to the foot of the bed and sits.*) Matter of fact I think we'll all have lots of chance for rest while we're here. Just between us, I think it's going to be pretty dull.

ELEANOR. (*Pulling her knees under her chin.*) We'll find plenty to do in the morning.

THEODORA. At home there would be people around, and lots of talk and laughter. Lights and excitement—that's for me.

ELEANOR. (*Seriously.*) I suppose I don't need such things. There never was much excitement while I was taking care of Mother. When she was asleep I'd play solitaire or listen to the radio. I couldn't read in the evenings, not after reading aloud to her every afternoon. Her illness went on for so many years.

THEODORA. (*Sympathetically.*) You make me feel foolish now. Shallow and selfish.

ELEANOR. Why should you?

THEODORA. Because I worry about there being nothing to amuse me. Tell me how horrible I am.

ELEANOR. (*Obediently.*) You're horrible.

THEODORA. But you are sweet and pleasant, and everyone likes you very much. Luke has fallen in love with you—and I'm jealous.

ELEANOR. (*Amused.*) What nonsense.

THEODORA. Not at all. Now I want to know more about you. Did you really have to take care of your mother for a long time?

ELEANOR. Eleven years, until she died three months ago.

THEODORA. Were you sorry when she died? Should I say how sorry I am?

ELEANOR. (*Quietly.*) No. She wasn't very happy.

THEODORA. And neither were you.

ELEANOR. (*Nodding.*) And neither was I.

THEODORA. What about now? What did you do when she died?

25

ELEANOR. Sold the house, and everything else that my sister didn't want.

THEODORA. Everything?

ELEANOR. Just as soon as I could.

THEODORA. (*Gaily.*) And then you started the mad, gay fling that brought you inevitably to Hill House?

ELEANOR. (*Dryly.*) Not exactly.

THEODORA. (*Surprised.*) But after all those wasted years. Didn't you go on a cruise, or look for exciting young men, or buy new clothes,—something?

ELEANOR. Unfortunately there wasn't much money. I did buy *some* new clothes. To come to Hill House.

THEODORA. What about when you go back? Do you have a job?

ELEANOR. No, no job right now. I don't know quite what I'll do.

THEODORA. I know what *I'm* going to do. I'm going to turn on every light in the apartment and just bask. (*She gets up.*)

ELEANOR. What is your apartment like?

THEODORA. (*Shrugging.*) Nice. It's an old place, but we fixed it up ourselves, my roommate and I. We painted it red and white and made over a lot of old furniture we dug up in junk shops. We both love doing over old things. (*Pause.*) Tell me where *you* live.

ELEANOR. (*Slowly, with uncertainty.*) I have a little place of my own. Like yours, only I live alone. I'm still furnishing it, buying things one at a time so they'll be just right. Everything has to be exactly the way I want it, because there's only me to use it. Right now I'm looking for a blue cup with stars painted on the inside. I had one when I was a little girl. When you looked into it, after the milk was all gone, it seemed full of stars. I want a cup like that again.

THEODORA. Maybe I'll find one for you. Then I can send it to you. Someday you'll get a little package saying "To Eleanor, with love from her friend Theodora," and it will be a blue cup full of stars. (*Pause.*) But right now Theodora is sleepy. What do you say to bed time?

ELEANOR. I wonder if the others are in bed?

THEODORA. Most likely. The Doctor's probably reading a horror story—for relaxation.

ELEANOR. I'll bet their doors are locked. Mine is.

THEODORA. (*Crossing towards the* D. R. *door.*) Mine, too. But

I'll leave this one ajar. If you feel the least bit nervous call out, promise?

ELEANOR. I will. And Theo? Thank you for talking. It won't really be dull here. Not if we have each other to talk to.

THEODORA. (*Smiling.*) Good night.

ELEANOR. Good night. Sleep tight. (*Theodora exits* D. R., *leaving the door ajar behind her. Eleanor takes off her robe and drapes it over the end of the bed, crosses to the bureau as if to put out the light, then hesitates and decides to leave it on. She gets into bed and pulls up the covers. After she has composed herself for sleep the light on the bureau dims slowly to denote the passage of time. Then Eleanor begins to toss about, murmuring to herself, as though having a nightmare. Her words become louder and more distinct. As she calls out in her sleep the bureau light gradually comes up again.*) Coming, Mother, coming. (*Louder.*) It's all right, I'm coming. (*Frantically.*) Just a minute— I'm coming! (*She tosses about feverishly.*)

THEODORA. (*Off* R.) Eleanor?

ELEANOR. (*Sitting up suddenly, her eyes open wide in terror.*) Coming, Mother— I'm coming!

THEODORA. (*At the door,* D. R.) Eleanor—did you hear it?

ELEANOR. (*Coming into focus.*) What? What? Theodora?

THEODORA. (*Crossing to the bed.*) Was it just my imagination? Didn't you hear it?

ELEANOR. (*Confused.*) Hear what? What's wrong?

THEODORA. (*Calmly.*) Something is knocking on the doors. (*Eleanor reacts in fright.*) Down at the other end of the hall. (*She senses Eleanor's fear.*) I didn't mean to upset you—probably the Doctor and Luke are there already to see what's going on. It just . . . surprised me, that's all. I was fast asleep.

ELEANOR. (*Holding up her hand for silence, she listens attentively. Then, in a small voice.*) Theodora, it's getting closer.

THEODORA. (*Moving closer to Eleanor.*) Only a noise, that's all it can be. (*Puzzled.*) Listen, it has an echo. (*They both listen closely. From off* U. R. *comes a distant, hollow, thumping sound, as though the doors were being hit with an iron kettle, or iron bar. There is a pattern of regular thumping for a minute, then a soft tapping, and finally a quick flurry of energetic, impatient pounding. The cycle is repeated on each door—coming gradually nearer.*)

27

Eleanor and Theodora listen in horrified fascination, speechless and transfixed.)

ELEANOR. *(After an eternity of listening. Terror in her voice.)* Where are they? Why don't they come?

THEODORA. *(Whispering.)* Maybe it will go on down the other side of the hall. *(The pounding is suddenly heard again, very close, as though it were at the door across the hall. It grows louder—almost deafening.)*

ELEANOR. *(Leaping from the bed and rushing to the door she holds both hands against it desperately.)* Go away! Go away! *(Theodora crosses to her and puts her arm around her protectively. The pounding stops.)*

THEODORA. *(After a moment.)* There, you see—it's gone. *(Eleanor shivers.)* You poor kid, you're freezing. Come on—back to bed with you. *(She pulls Eleanor towards the bed.)*

ELEANOR. I'm cold . . . deadly cold.

THEODORA. So am I. *(Getting Eleanor back into bed, she pulls the covers up around her.)* There. Warmer now?

ELEANOR. *(Shaken.)* Where's Luke? Where's the doctor?

THEODORA. *(Quietly.)* I don't know. Are you warmer?

ELEANOR. *(Shivering.)* No.

THEODORA. *(Reassuringly.)* In a minute I'll go out in the hall and call them. Are you— *(She is interrupted by the thumping, this time on the bedroom door, U. R., and extremely loud. The door shakes under the blows. Eleanor pulls back in terror and Theodora, her composure shattered, huddles against her. They both turn towards the door in horrid fascination, their eyes moving up to the top—where the pounding appears to be centered. They cling together for safety and warmth as the banging builds to a deafening crescendo. After an interminable moment it begins to taper off. Theodora relaxes slightly.)* Is it stopping?

ELEANOR. *(Moaning.)* No. It's found us. It was looking for someone, and it found us.

THEODORA. *(Indicating silence.)* Ssh! *(She listens closely.)*

ELEANOR. Now I know why people scream, because I think I'm going to.

THEODORA. I will if you will—wait! *(She listens again. There is the sound of small patting noises around the door frame, as though whatever is outside were trying to find a way to sneak in. The door knob turns, slowly, then insistently.)* Are you *sure* it's locked? (*Eleanor nods nervously. Then the pounding starts again, this time moving the door ominously against its hinges.*)

ELEANOR. (*Shouting.*) You can't get in. (*There is a sudden silence, and then a small, unearthly giggle from beyond the door. Theodora and Eleanor together again, holding their breath. Then the giggle is gone and, after a moment of total silence, the voices of Luke and Dr. Montague are heard in the distance, off R. Theodora is visibly relieved.*)

THEODORA. (*Straightening up.*) We've been clutching each other like a couple of lost children. Are you all right?

ELEANOR. (*Still shaken.*) Is it really over?

THEODORA. For tonight, anyway. Can't you tell? Aren't you warm again, all of a sudden?

ELEANOR. (*Shivering.*) Yes. Warmer.

THEODORA. (*The voices of Luke and Dr. Montague are heard in the hall. Theodora rises and crosses to the door.*) Here come Luke and the doctor. I'll let them in.

ELEANOR. (*Imploring.*) Don't let them knock . . . please. I couldn't bear it.

THEODORA. (*Patiently.*) All right. Try to relax now. We're safe. (*She opens the door.*) This way, gentlemen. We're in here.

LUKE. (*Outside the door. Facetiously.*) Why—you look as though you'd seen a ghost.

THEODORA. Very funny. Come in.

LUKE. (*Calling down the hall.*) They're both in Eleanor's room, Doctor. (*He enters.*)

THEODORA. Well, how do you like living in a haunted house?

LUKE. (*Pleasantly.*) It's perfectly fine. Gives me an excuse to have a drink in the middle of the night. (*He brandishes a flask.*) Could I interest you? (*Before either can answer, Dr. Montague enters.*)

DR. MONTAGUE. (*Concerned.*) Are you all right? Did anything happen in here while we were outside? (*Eleanor gets up from the bed, pulling her robe around her. She is calmer now.*)

THEODORA. (*Airily.*) No, nothing in particular. Someone knocked on the door with a cannon ball and then tried to get in and eat us, and started laughing its head off when we wouldn't open the door. But nothing really out of the way. (*Dr. Montague looks puzzled.*)

ELEANOR. (*Crossing to the door and examining it on the out-*

29

side.) I thought the whole door was going to shatter. But there isn't even a scratch on the wood. It's still perfectly smooth. (*Dr. Montague turns to study the door.*)

THEODORA. How nice it didn't mar the woodwork. I couldn't bear it if this dear old house got hurt. Nell here was going to scream.

ELEANOR. (*Quickly.*) So were you.

THEODORA. Not at all. I only said that to keep you company. Besides, Mrs. Dudley already said she wouldn't come. (*Turning to the men.*) And where were *you*, our manly defenders?

LUKE. We were chasing a dog, or at least some animal *like* a dog. We followed it outside. (*Theodora stares.*)

ELEANOR. (*Unbelieving.*) You mean it was *inside?*

DR. MONTAGUE. (*Turning from the door.*) I saw it run past my door. Just a glimpse of it slipping by. I woke Luke and we followed it down the stairs and out into the garden. We lost it somewhere back of the house. '

ELEANOR. The front door was open?

LUKE. (*Slightly puzzled.*) No, it was closed. So were all the other doors. We checked. (*He turns to Dr. Montague, as if for an explanation.*)

DR. MONTAGUE. (*Stroking his beard for a moment.*) Could it be . . . you see, we've been wandering around outside for quite a while. We never dreamed that you ladies were awake until we heard your voices. (*Pause. To Theodora.*) Your story makes me wonder about something—something that, perhaps, we haven't taken into account. (*The others regard him questioningly.*) Let me explain. It's clear that Luke and I were awakened earlier than you ladies, perhaps deliberately. We have been up and about, inside and out, for better than two hours—led on what seems to have been a wild goose chase. But, during all that time, neither of us (*He glances at Luke.*) heard *any* sound up here until just a few minutes ago. It was perfectly quiet. But then, when we gave up our search and decided to come upstairs, we heard your voices. Now it appears that in coming we drove away whatever was waiting outside your door. And now again, while we remain together, all is quiet.

THEODORA. (*Frowning.*) I don't quite see what you're driving at.

DR. MONTAGUE. (*Quietly.*) We must take precautions.

LUKE. Precautions?

ELEANOR. Against what? How?

DR. MONTAGUE. (*Slowly, and with emphasis.*) Let me put it this way. When Luke and I are lured *outside*, and you two are kept imprisoned *inside*, doesn't it begin to seem . . . (*He looks from face to face.*) doesn't it begin to seem that the intention is . . . somehow . . . to separate us? (*He speaks the last words with great care. The others stare at him in thoughtful silence. Then Eleanor, concern written on her face, crosses slowly to the bed and sits, pulling her robe more closely around her as the others turn to watch her and*)

THE CURTAIN FALLS

ACT TWO

Scene One

Late morning, several days later. The bedroom area is dark, while the parlor is illuminated by its various, heavy-shaded lamps. As it is an interior room there is no trace of sunlight although the gloom of the room is somewhat relieved by a fire which glows softly in the fireplace.

As the curtain rises, Eleanor is alone on the stage. She is curled in one of the D. L. chairs, a book open on her lap, and a coffee cup on the table between the chairs. She looks up from her reading as the double doors open, U. C., and Theodora pokes her head in.

THEODORA. Nell? (*Seeing her.*) Oh, there you are. We were worried about you.

ELEANOR. (*Matter of fact.*) I had enough chatter.

THEODORA. (*Coming in.*) You're getting quite brave. You know our rule—no one is to go off alone.

ELEANOR. (*Putting down her book.*) I can find my way in here safely enough. Anyway, it's worth the risk to get away from Luke's silly talk for awhile.

THEODORA. (*Sitting on the sofa. With a laugh.*) Is it *that* bad? Good heavens, that makes me feel shallow. I find him rather amusing.

ELEANOR. (*Defensively.*) You know what I mean. He's never . . . *serious* about anything.

THEODORA. (*Twitting her.*) Maybe he's compensating for a deep-seated insecurity. After all, he did say that he never had a mother, poor boy.

ELEANOR. (*Finishing her coffee.*) That's no excuse for treating *everything* as a joke.

THEODORA. (*Lightly.*) Including you, perhaps? Could be you wish Luke was a little more . . . shall we say . . . aggressively

32

friendly? After all, he's not exactly ugly. (*Eleanor makes a face, and goes back to reading.*) Not that? Well then, maybe you object to Luke's attitude about this whole haunted house thing. He does treat it all pretty lightly, doesn't he? Maybe if *his* door got pounded on.

ELEANOR. (*Testily.*) You know how I feel about *that*.

THEODORA. Do I?

ELEANOR. (*Putting down her book again.*) I agree with Dr. Montague. These supernatural manifestations reflect certain qualities of Hill House—and would probably occur no matter who happened to be here. They have nothing to do with us in particular and I, for one, have decided not to let them bother me.

THEODORA. (*Quietly.*) I think you *want* to mean that. (*Eleanor glances at her sharply. Theodora adds quickly.*) Matter of fact, though, I'm beginning to think that this curious life agrees with you. You look radiant.

ELEANOR. (*Mollified.*) So do you.

THEODORA. (*Pleased.*) Really? (*Thoughtfully.*) That is strange, isn't it? By rights we ought to be going around looking haggard, with dark circles under our eyes—but here we are, two blooming, fresh young lovelies.

ELEANOR. Not quite. Not at my age. "Freshness" is a flatterer's word when you're nearing thirty.

THEODORA. Oh? Well, you look about fourteen. (*Eleanor makes a wry face and goes back to her book. The doors open again and Luke enters, followed by Dr. Montague. Theodora turns at their entrance.*)

LUKE. May we join you? Our discussion of world affairs has grown rather stale without the feminine point of view to leaven it. (*He turns to Dr. Montague.*) Right, Doctor?

DR. MONTAGUE. Exactly my thoughts.

THEODORA. (*With a glance at Eleanor.*) Flatterers. You know very well you've been going over what happened the other night. Any answers yet? (*Eleanor puts down her book as they seat themselves—Dr. Montague on the sofa, Luke in the chair beside her.*)

DR. MONTAGUE. No conclusive ones. But, and this may or may not be related, I find that I'm sleeping wonderfully well—and that food tastes better than ever.

LUKE. Perhaps Mrs. Dudley is surpassing herself.

DR. MONTAGUE. (*With a shrug.*) Whatever the explanation, I

33

consider it uniquely exciting to be a part of something so fraught with psychic potential. There should be a great deal to report to the "outside world" when our investigations are concluded.

ELEANOR. (*Vaguely.*) Is there *still* a world out there? I'm sure Mrs. Dudley goes somewhere else at night, and it must be that our food comes from a place with stores, and lights, and people, but as far as I can clearly remember there is no other place than this.

LUKE. (*To Eleanor, with a smile.*) We are on a desert island.

ELEANOR. (*Ignoring Luke.*) I can't picture *any* world but Hill House.

THEODORA. Perhaps we should makes notches on a stick, or pile pebbles in a heap so we'll know how long we've been marooned.

LUKE. (*To the others.*) Actually, I find it quite pleasant not having any word from outside . . . No letters, no newspapers. (*With emphasis.*) *Think* what might be happening out there.

DR. MONTAGUE. We'll soon know what's going on. As I mentioned to you, Mrs. Montague will be here this morning.

LUKE. (*Gallant.*) We'll be delighted to see her, of course.

THEODORA. I imagine she's holding high hopes of things going bump in the night. Maybe Hill House will outdo itself and greet her with a volley of psychic experiences.

DR. MONTAGUE. (*With a twinkle.*) Mrs. Montague will be more than ready to receive them, I assure you.

ELEANOR. (*Seriously.*) It's been so quiet. Perhaps Hill House is biding its time until she arrives.

LUKE. (*To Eleanor, again.*) Or waiting until *we* feel secure—so it can pounce on us.

ELEANOR. (*To Dr. Montague.*) I've been trying to remember more about the other night. I can recall *knowing* that I was frightened—but I can't imagine actually *being* frightened.

THEODORA. (*Shivering.*) I remember the cold.

ELEANOR. (*Intently.*) I think it's because it was so unreal by any pattern of thought I'm used to. I mean, it just didn't make *sense.* (*Dr. Montague nods.*)

LUKE. (*Affably.*) I agree. This morning I had to convince myself again that it all happened. Almost the reverse of a bad dream, where you keep telling yourself that it *didn't* really happen.

THEODORA. (*Firmly.*) Well, I thought it was exciting.

DR. MONTAGUE. (*Lifting a finger in warning.*) Remember—it

is still perfectly possible that it was all caused by subterranean waters, or some such phenomenon. Mrs. Montague will certainly have more thoughts along that line when she arrives.

THEODORA. Then hooray for secret springs, I say.

DR. MONTAGUE. (*Concerned.*) I wish you were not quite so positive about that. What you feel is exciting for sure, but might it not also be dangerous? Perhaps an effect of the atmosphere of Hill House? The first sign that we might have—as it were—fallen under a spell?

THEODORA. Why not? I shall be an enchanted princess.

LUKE. (*Seriously.*) And yet, if the other night is a true measure of Hill House, we aren't going to have any real trouble. We *were* frightened, of course, and the experience was unpleasant while it was going on. But I can't remember that I sensed any *physical* danger. (*Archly.*) Even when Theodora said that whatever was outside her door was coming to *eat* her.

ELEANOR. (*Quickly.*) But I know what she meant. It was exactly the right word. I had the strange feeling that it wanted to consume us, take us into itself, make us a part of the house . . . (*She hesitates, as though unable to express herself completely.*)

THEODORA. (*To Eleanor.*) I thought you were the girl who wasn't bothered by all this. (*Eleanor looks flustered.*)

DR. MONTAGUE. (*Positively.*) No physical danger exists, I can assure you of that. No ghost in all the long histories of ghosts has ever hurt anyone physically. The only damage is done by the victim to *himself.* One cannot even say that the ghost attacks the mind, because the mind, the conscious, thinking mind, is invulnerable. In all our conscious minds, as we sit here talking, there is not one iota of real belief in ghosts. (*He looks at the others for a moment.*) No, the menace of the supernatural is that it attacks where modern minds are weakest, where we have abandoned our protective armor of superstition, without developing a substitute defense. Not one of us thinks rationally that what ran through the garden was a ghost, or that what knocked on the door was a ghost, and yet there was certainly something going on in Hill House. But the mind's instinctive refuge—self doubt—is eliminated, and neither can we say that it was "imagination." After all, three others were there, too.

ELEANOR. (*Rising, crossing* R.) I *could* say that all three of you are in my imagination—that none of this is real.

35

DR. MONTAGUE. (*Gravely.*) If I thought that you could really believe that, I'd send you home this morning. You would be coming far too close to the state of mind which would welcome the perils of Hill House . . . with a kind of sisterly embrace.

THEODORA. He means he would think you were batty, Nell dear.

ELEANOR. (*Turning.*) Well, I suppose I would be. If I had to take sides with Hill House against the rest of you, I'd expect you to send me away.

DR. MONTAGUE. (*Glancing briefly at Eleanor.*) Poltergeists are another thing altogether. They deal entirely with the physical world. They throw stones, they move objects, they smash dishes. But they are also the rock-bottom of the supernatural social scale —destructive, but mindless. And will-less too. They are merely undirected force. (*Smiling.*) Do you recall Oscar Wilde's story, "The Canterville Ghost?"

THEODORA. The American twins who routed the fine old English ghost?

DR. MONTAGUE. Exactly. I have always liked the notion that the American twins were actually a poltergeist phenomenon. Certainly poltergeists can overshadow more interesting manifestations. Bad ghosts drive out good, you might say. (*Suddenly Eleanor laughs nervously. The others look at her quickly.*) Does that amuse you? I can give you a good many documented instances, you know.

ELEANOR. I'm sure you can, Doctor. And I apologize if I seemed to be rude. It's just that I was suddenly aware of how *serious* this all is to us and yet I know that no one outside would believe a word of what we say.

DR. MONTAGUE. Perhaps not.

THEODORA. Well, I'm fascinated, and I say on with it. (*Turning to Dr. Montague.*) What shall we do today?

DR. MONTAGUE. (*Smiling.*) Really, you *are* a pack of children. Always asking me what to do today. Can't you amuse yourselves? I have work to do.

LUKE. Don't forget the cold spot, Doctor.

DR. MONTAGUE. Ah, yes. There's your answer. You're welcome to help Luke and myself measure the cold spot in the nursery doorway.

ELEANOR. No thank you.

THEODORA. All I *really* want to do is to slide down that wonderful bannister in the front hall.

LUKE. Or how about a game of hide and seek?

DR. MONTAGUE. (*Rising.*) Well, try not to wander around alone too much. I can't think of a good reason why not, but it does seem sensible.

THEODORA. (*With mock menace.*) Because there are bears in the woods.

ELEANOR. And tigers in the attic.

LUKE. And an old witch in the tower—*plus* a dragon in the drawing room.

DR. MONTAGUE. (*With a laugh.*) But I'm quite serious— I agree that we mustn't let our imaginations run riot, but then again there is no reason to be foolhardy either . . . (*He is interrupted by the opening of the double doors, u. c. Mrs. Dudley appears in the doorway. The others turn to look at her.*) Yes? Did you want something, Mrs. Dudley?

MRS. DUDLEY. (*Without expression.*) I clear after breakfast. I made that plain when you came.

DR. MONTAGUE. (*Puzzled.*) And? I believe it's the dining room that needs clearing.

MRS. DUDLEY. It's clear. But there's a cup and saucer gone. I have to put them all back on the shelves each time . . . it's what I agreed to do.

DR. MONTAGUE. Now just a moment, Mrs. Dudley. Are you suggesting . . .

ELEANOR. (*Interrupting.*) It's all right, Doctor. (*She crosses L. and retrieves the missing cup and saucer from the small table between the chairs at L.*) I'm afraid I'm the guilty party. I finished my coffee in here.

MRS. DUDLEY. (*Still in the doorway.*) I clear after breakfast. I set lunch at one. Dinner I set on at six. And I clear each time. (*Eleanor crosses u. with the cup and saucer, and hands them to Mrs. Dudley.*)

DR. MONTAGUE. (*Sternly.*) Mrs. Dudley . . .

MRS. DUDLEY. (*Interrupting*) They *all* go back on the shelves—each time. That's the way it's done.

DR. MONTAGUE. (*After regarding the unyielding, granitic Mrs. Dudley for a moment. Piqued.*) Of course. We mustn't interfere with your duties. (*Mrs. Dudley turns and exits. Theodora titters.*)

37

THEODORA. *Really.* That woman is beyond belief.

ELEANOR. (*Aping Mrs. Dudley.*) At eleven o'clock I feed the vampires. It's part of what I agreed to.

LUKE. (*Also imitating Mrs. Dudley.*) I don't wait on people— just vampires. (*They all laugh.*)

DR. MONTAGUE. (*Recovering his good humor.*) Now, now, we mustn't make fun of Mrs. Dudley. She does what she agreed to do. (*More laughter.*) No— I mean it. (*Pause. He crosses to the sofa, sits.*) But she *is* annoying, I'll admit. (*He looks up defiantly.*) And now I suddenly find that what I want most is more coffee. What do you say we demand it, and see what happens?

ELEANOR. You mean go right in there and ask Mrs. Dudley?

THEODORA. Walk right up to her when it isn't one o'clock or six o'clock and just *ask* for coffee?

DR. MONTAGUE. Yes, I think so. (*To Luke.*) Luke, my boy, I have observed that you are already something of a favorite with Mrs. Dudley.

LUKE. (*Amazed.*) And how did you ever manage to observe anything so unlikely? Mrs. Dudley regards me with the same particular loathing (*He glances at Eleanor.*) she gives a cup and saucer not in their proper places at the proper time.

DR. MONTAGUE. Well you are, after all, the heir to the house. Mrs. Dudley must feel for you as an old family retainer feels for the young master.

LUKE. You *are* a romantic sort, Doctor. But I assure you that in Mrs. Dudley's estimation I am lower than a dropped fork. If you are really serious about asking the old fool for something send Theo, or our charming Nell. *They* aren't afraid.

THEODORA. No you don't. You can't send a helpless female to face down Mrs. Dudley. Nell and I are here to be protected . . . not to man the battlements for you cowards.

LUKE. (*Turning to Dr. Montague.*) Well then, you Doctor . . .

DR. MONTAGUE. (*Quickly.*) Oh come now. You wouldn't really think of asking me, an older man. Anyway, you *know* she adores you.

LUKE. (*Shaking his head.*) Dear, dear. You're willing to sacrifice me for a cup of coffee. (*He rises.*) Well, do not be surprised— and I say it darkly—do not be surprised if you lose your Luke in this cause. Perhaps Mrs. Dudley hasn't yet had her own mid-morning snack, and she is perfectly capable of a *filet de Luke a la meuniere. (He crosses* U. C. *to the double doors. Turning.)* If I do not return, I entreat you . . . regard your lunch with the gravest suspicion. *(He bows and exits. Theodora stretches luxuriously.)*

THEODORA. Lovely Luke.

ELEANOR. Lovely Hill House.

DR. MONTAGUE. *(Shaking his head.)* Lovely way to use up a morning when I should be working on my notes.

ELEANOR. *(Sitting in one of the* L. *chairs.)* You know, I wonder —why *has* everything been so quiet since that night? It's nerve-wracking . . . almost *worse* than having something happen.

THEODORA. It's not *us* doing the waiting. It's the house biding its time.

DR. MONTAGUE. Until we feel secure, perhaps? As Luke suggested.

ELEANOR. I wonder how long it can wait before it pounces. I'm almost tempted to write a letter to my sister. You know— "Having perfectly *splendid* time here in jolly old Hill House . . ."

THEODORA. You really *must* plan to bring the whole family next summer. We sleep under blankets every night . . .

ELEANOR. The air is so bracing, particularly in the doorway of the nursery . . .

THEODORA. You go around all the time just glad to be alive . . . still alive, that is . . .

ELEANOR. There's something going on every minute . . .

THEODORA. And so *far* from the madding crowd. *(They laugh. Theodora glances at Dr. Montague, who suddenly looks concerned.)* What is it, Doctor? Too *much* female leavening?

DR. MONTAGUE. *(Rising.)* I broke my own first rule; I sent him alone. *(He crosses* U. C.*)* I'd better make sure . . . *(The double doors open as he nears them. Luke steps in, his face solemn.)*

LUKE. It's all right. I'm safe enough. But come into the long hall-way. I've found something more interesting than coffee. *(Eleanor and Theodora rise, sobered by his tone of voice.)* Do you have your flashlight? *(Dr. Montague nods. He exits, the others follow. After a moment they all re-enter. Eleanor, ashen-faced, crosses slowly to the sofa and sits. Theodora come after her and stands by the sofa.)*

THEODORA. *(Quietly.)* Did you read it? *(Eleanor nods, her face a mingling of fear and anguish.)*

39

DR. MONTAGUE. (*Bemused.*) Chalk. It was written in chalk. How strange. (*Turning to Luke.*) We must copy it—exactly as it is.

LUKE. (*Taking a piece of paper out of his pocket.*) I already have. (*Reads, with a glance at Eleanor.*) "Help, Eleanor . . . come home." (*Pause.*) I've never seen such *enormous* writing. It stretches down the entire hall.

ELEANOR. (*Plaintively.*) Please, wipe it off. Please. It's . . . crazy.

THEODORA. (*Putting her hand on Eleanor's shoulder.*) Crazy is the word all right. (*Eleanor shivers.*) Just take it easy. Luke will see that it's wiped off.

LUKE. Of course, right away. (*He rises.*) I'll ask Mrs. Dudley. (*He exits,* U. C.)

ELEANOR. (*Shaking her head.*) But it's crazy. *Why*—?

DR. MONTAGUE. (*Crossing to Eleanor.*) Now you listen to me . . . Just because your name . . .

ELEANOR. (*Sitting up.*) That's it. (*Staring at Dr. Montague.*) It knows my name, doesn't it? It knows *my* name.

THEODORA. (*Shaking Eleanor's shoulders.*) Stop it—will you? It could have said any of us. It knows *all* our names.

ELEANOR. (*Looking up at Theodora.*) Did you write it? Please tell me. I won't be angry, I promise you. I just want to know that it was only a joke—to frighten me. (*She turns to Dr. Montague.*)

DR. MONTAGUE. (*Quietly.*) You know that none of us wrote it. (*Luke re-enters.*)

ELEANOR. (*Turning to Luke.*) Luke, you wrote it, didn't you? When you went out?

LUKE. (*Crossing* D. *and sitting on the arm of the sofa.*) Listen, you think I go around writing your name everywhere? Scrawling "Eleanor, Eleanor" all over the walls? (*He gives her shoulder a little shake.*) I've got more sense. Behave yourself.

ELEANOR. (*Looking from one to the other.*) Then why *me*? Have I done something to attract attention? More than anyone else?

THEODORA. (*Rising, and crossing* L.) I don't think so, dear. (*She turns and looks at Eleanor.*) Maybe you wrote it yourself.

ELEANOR. (*Rising, almost shouting.*) You think I *want* to see my name scribbled all over this foul house? You think I *like* being singled out—

THEODORA. (*Lightly.*) It was asking for help—did you notice? (*Cuttingly.*) Perhaps the spirit of the poor, bedeviled companion has found a means of communication at last. Maybe she was only waiting for some drab, timid—

ELEANOR. (*Breaking in.*) Maybe it was only addressed to me because no appeal for help could possibly get through that iron selfishness of *yours*.

THEODORA. (*Levelly.*) And maybe, of course, you wrote it yourself.

ELEANOR. (*Vehemently.*) Don't say that, do you hear! Don't! (*The two men have remained apart from this exchange. Now Luke steps forward.*)

LUKE. (*Firmly.*) That's enough, Eleanor.

ELEANOR. (*Turning on him. Stamping her foot.*) How dare you? How dare you? (*There is a sudden silence. Eleanor sinks down on the sofa, covering her face with her hands.*)

THEODORA. (*Crossing to her, solicitously.*) Nell, dear. I am sorry. (*She puts her hands on Eleanor's shoulders. After a moment Eleanor looks up at her and smiles sheepishly.*)

ELEANOR. I'm sorry. I was frightened.

DR. MONTAGUE. (*Comfortingly.*) Of course you were. We understand.

THEODORA. (*Sitting beside Eleanor.*) I really thought you were going to crack up. I would have in your place. I just tried to shock you out of it. We can't afford to lose you, you know.

ELEANOR. (*Looking at her hands.*) Thanks. I guess I was sort of . . . shaky for a minute. (*She glances at Luke.*)

LUKE. I wondered if you two were going to come to blows, until I realized what Theodora was doing. Anger overcomes fear.

ELEANOR. (*With a little laugh.*) Long-lost cousins? Fighting?

DR. MONTAGUE. Try to put it out of your mind, my dear. Remember our agreement. We must work together, keep accurate notes, and take nothing personally. Our purpose here is objective and scientific.

ELEANOR. (*Apologetically.*) I know. Hysterical females aren't much use to you.

DR. MONTAGUE. You're hardly that, I assure you. (*He crosses u. c.*) But you did have a nasty shock. Why don't you and Theodora stay here off the "firing line" for a bit, while Luke and I go up and measure that very intriguing cold spot upstairs? (*To Luke.*) Will you join me?

LUKE. (*Crossing* U. C.) Delighted. Maybe we'll catch the "mad scribbler" chalk in hand.

DR. MONTAGUE. (*Chuckling.*) I hardly think so. (*To the girls.*) You know where we'll be. If you want us for *any* reason, call out. Do you promise?

THEODORA. Aye aye, sir. (*Eleanor nods. The men exit. After a moment Eleanor gets up and turns to Theodora.*)

ELEANOR. I never *really* thought you did it. Honestly. What a silly fool I am.

THEODORA. (*Dismissing it.*) I don't blame you a bit. I would have been petrified. Now let's forget it. (*She crosses* U. L. *to the desk and picks up a large book.*) Have you seen this? (*Eleanor looks blank.*) It's *unbelievable.* Dr. Montague says it's a scrapbook that Hugh Crain put together for his daughters—for their education and enlightenment, of all things. (*She crosses to the sofa with the book.*) Come on, sit down and put your mind on someone *else's* troubles. (*Eleanor joins Theodora on the sofa, as she opens the book and points to the first entry.*) Lesson one—humility. Illustrated by a delightful Goya etching of some poor things being disemboweled. (*Eleanor looks at the book.*)

ELEANOR. (*Recoiling.*) It's awful.

THEODORA. But there's *more.* An inscription by Hugh Crain himself. (*She reads.*) "Honor thy father and thy mother, upon whom a heavy charge has been laid, that they lead their children in innocence and righteousness along the fearful narrow path to everlasting bliss." He should have added, "or else."

ELEANOR. Poor kids.

THEODORA. (*Flipping the page.*) Next comes hell. Don't look if you're squeamish.

ELEANOR. I think I'll skip hell.

THEODORA. You're wise. The illustration is one of the less attractive deaths, with some words of wisdom about agony and screaming and undying pain.

ELEANOR. He probably read it aloud every night at bed time.

THEODORA. (*Turning more pages.*) And *now,* the seven deadly sins. Looks like the old boy drew these himself.

ELEANOR. (*Glancing at the book.*) He really put his heart into gluttony. I'm not sure I'll ever be hungry again.

THEODORA. Wait till last. He really outdid himself. (*She turns the page.*) Here.

ELEANOR. (*Looking at the book in horror.*) Good heavens!

THEODORA. He *must* have drawn it himself.

ELEANOR. For *children!*

THEODORA. (*Lightly.*) Their very own scrapbook. (*She turns to the end of the book.*) The last page is the nicest, I think. He signed it in his own blood. Want to see it?

ELEANOR. (*Rising.*) No thank you.

THEODORA. No? It's really quite edifying. Something about sacred pacts being written in blood, and instructions to his daughters about living virtuously and being preserved from the pitfalls of this world. In blood! Can you imagine it?

ELEANOR. He must have enjoyed it. Signing his name in his own blood.

THEODORA. Not exactly healthy work for a grown man.

ELEANOR. (*Turning.*) But they must have been very small when their father left Hill House. The girls, I mean. Maybe he never read it to them.

THEODORA. Oh, but I'm sure he did. Leaning over their cradles, and spitting out the words so they would take root in their little minds. (*She closes the book and rises.*) Hugh Crain, you were a dirty old man, and you made a dirty old house. (*She whirls around, calling to the walls.*) If you can still hear me from anywhere, I would like to tell you to your face that I genuinely hope you will spend eternity in that foul, horrible hell you pictured so accurately for your children. And may you never stop burning for a minute. (*She laughs, but Eleanor crosses to her quickly and grasps her arm.*)

ELEANOR. (*Tensely.*) Stop! (*Theodora looks at her questioningly.*) Do you hear it?

THEODORA. (*Uncertain.*) What? Do I hear what?

ELEANOR. (*Quietly.*) It's laughing. (*Frowning.*) Why is it laughing? (*Theodora looks at Eleanor apprehensively. Eleanor signals her to be silent. They listen a moment, and then there comes the sound of a low, muffled laugh from off L., behind the small door to the tower. It is a soft, disembodied laugh, which rises up the scale and then breaks off with a little gasp. Eleanor takes a step L., towards the door.*) Stop! Do you hear me? (*Pause. Then with a note of desperation in her voice.*) Go away! Go away and leave me alone! (*The laughing stops.*)

THEODORA. (*Coming up behind Eleanor.*) It's all right, Nell. There's no danger. (*As she speaks, the laughing starts in again, building gradually to a deafening intensity. When she can stand no more, Eleanor screams, and the stage is abruptly plunged into darkness. There is a long, aching silence and then, from off L., comes the sound of a small child crying.*)

ELEANOR. (*In the darkness. Pleading.*) Please, please don't hurt her. I'll do whatever you ask, but don't hurt her. Let her go. (*Silence, and then the crying begins again.*) STOP IT! Do you hear? You must stop it. (*The crying grows louder and more desperate.*) Oh please, please! I can't stand it. You must stop. Theodora—make it stop. (*She sobs. Gradually the crying fades out, and the lights slowly come up again. Then the U. C. doors open, and Dr. Montague enters, followed by Theodora and Luke. He crosses quickly to Eleanor, who kneels near the sofa, and helps her up.*)

DR. MONTAGUE. It's all right, my dear—you're perfectly safe now. (*Eleanor looks at him dazedly, and then turns her head towards Theodora.*)

ELEANOR. Theo? (*Pause.*) Weren't you here with me, Theo?

THEODORA. I went to get Dr. Montague. I didn't *want* to leave you alone. I had no choice.

ELEANOR. (*Still dazed.*) Alone? You left me alone?

THEODORA. I'm sorry, Nell dear.

ELEANOR. (*Looking from one to the other. Slowly.*) Then whose hand was I holding? (*The others react.*) Do you hear me? *Whose hand was I holding?* (*As the others stand in shocked silence, Eleanor rushes to the small door at L., and pounds on it with her fists.*) Let her go, do you hear me? Let her go, let her go! (*The others rush after her, Dr. Montague pulls her away from the door.*)

DR. MONTAGUE. My dear, please. You *must* control yourself.

ELEANOR. (*Pleading.*) But it's in there. Do you understand? It's hurting a child. We must *do* something.

DR. MONTAGUE. Of course, of course. We will, I assure you. But we must be calm. We're of no use if we lose our heads. That is what Hill House wants. (*Eleanor begins to cry.*) There, there, my dear.

THEODORA. Poor Nell. You *have* had a morning. (*They begin*

44

to lead her R., *as the doors open,* U. C., *and Mrs. Dudley appears.*
Luke notices her first.)

LUKE. (*Annoyed.*) Yes? What is it, Mrs. Dudley?

MRS. DUDLEY. Mrs. Montague is here. Should she come in?

DR. MONTAGUE. (*Not registering at first.*) What? Mrs. Montague? Of course, of course. I'd completely forgotten. (*He crosses* U. C. *as Mrs. Dudley stands aside and motions for Mrs. Montague to enter. Dr. Montague meets her at the door. Mrs. Dudley exits.*) My dear, my dear. How nice that you got here. We were worried about you. (*He kisses Mrs. Montague on the cheek. She is a large, formidable woman, quite dominant and overpowering. It is quickly evident that, in the Montague household, she is in charge.*)

MRS. MONTAGUE. (*Entering.*) I said I'd be here this morning, didn't I? Did you ever know me *not* to come when I said I would? I brought Arthur.

DR. MONTAGUE. (*Without enthusiasm.*) Oh yes, Arthur.

MRS. MONTAGUE. Well, *somebody* had to drive. I hope you didn't expect me to come all the way out here by myself. You know perfectly well how tired I get. (*She looks past her husband to the others, who are now grouped by the sofa.*) How do you do.

DR. MONTAGUE. (*Turning to the others.*) My dear, these are my friends who have been staying in Hill House with me these past few days. Theodora, Eleanor Vance, Luke Sanderson. My wife, Mrs. Montague. (*They murmur civilly. Mrs. Montague nods. Then she steps to the door and calls out.*)

MRS. MONTAGUE. Put the bags down in the hall, Arthur. (*Turning back to Dr. Montague.*) We'll need someone to help with the luggage.

DR. MONTAGUE. (*Politely.*) Of course, my dear.

MRS. MONTAGUE. And I trust you planned on us for lunch.

DR. MONTAGUE. Oh yes. I alerted Mrs. Dudley.

THEODORA. (*Imitating Mrs. Dudley.*) I set lunch at one o'clock. That's what I agreed to do. (*Eleanor, while still shaken, manages a slight smile.*)

MRS. MONTAGUE. (*Stepping* D.) What's that? (*Theodora laughs.*) Oh, I see. You're mimicking that ghastly woman who let us in. Let's see . . . you're . . .

THEODORA. Theodora.

MRS. MONTAGUE. Yes. Well, no matter. I'm sure I'll get to know all your names very soon. (*A meek but intense-looking little*

45

man of indeterminate age appears in the doorway, U. C. This is Arthur Parker. Mrs. Montague turns.) This gentleman is Arthur Parker. He drove me here, because I dislike driving myself. Arthur, these are John's friends.

ARTHUR. How do you do. (The others nod.)

MRS. MONTAGUE. (Looking directly at Luke.) I don't suppose we could do something about our bags now.

LUKE. (There is a pause, then Luke steps U., not overly pleased.) It would be a pleasure.

MRS. MONTAGUE. Thank you. I am to be in your most haunted room, of course. Arthur can go anywhere. The blue suitcase is mine, young man, and the small attaché case. (Luke looks at Dr. Montague inquiringly.)

DR. MONTAGUE. (To Luke.) The nursery, I think, for Mrs. Montague. (Luke nods. He and Arthur exit. To Mrs. Montague.) The nursery seems to be one source of disturbance. There's a definite cold spot in the doorway.

MRS. MONTAGUE. (Impatiently.) Is that all you have to report? It does seem to me that you haven't been very methodical. And I'll wager that you've done nothing with planchette. (Dr. Montague shakes his head.) Or automatic writing? (He shakes "No.") And I don't imagine that either of these young women has mediumistic gifts?

DR. MONTAGUE. Well . . .

MRS. MONTAGUE. (Stepping to the door she looks out and then calls off after Luke.) No, no. The brown bags are Arthur's. And the golf clubs. (To the others.) He brought them just in case. (She steps D.)

THEODORA. Just in case of what? (Mrs. Montague regards her coldly.)

DR. MONTAGUE. (Quickly.) As I mentioned—there's a very pronounced cold spot outside the nursery door.

MRS. MONTAGUE. Yes, dear. You said that. (She steps U. C. and peers out the doorway again. To Dr. Montague.) Isn't that young man going to help with Arthur's bags, too? (Dr. Montague shrugs.) You do seem to be in a state of confusion here, don't you? By this time I certainly thought you'd have things in some kind of order. Any figures materialize?

DR. MONTAGUE. There have been decided manifestations—

MRS. MONTAGUE. (*Ignoring him.*) Well, I'm here now, and we'll get things going right. Where is Arthur to put the car?

DR. MONTAGUE. There's an empty stable in back of the house. He can put it around later.

MRS. MONTAGUE. Nonsense. I do not believe in putting things off, John, as you know perfectly well. He can do it now. (*Nodding at Eleanor and Theodora.*) Perhaps one of these young ladies could show him the way.

DR. MONTAGUE. (*Hesitantly.*) The young ladies had a rather . . . shocking experience before you arrived. I think they'd rather stay here for the time being. (*Mrs. Montague is silent for a moment.*)

MRS. MONTAGUE. (*Looking at Theodora and Eleanor, and then to her husband.*) I must say, John, I sense a very definite nervousness here, which is *not* good. I deplore fear in these matters. You know perfectly well that those who have passed beyond *expect* to see us happy and smiling; they *want* to know that we are thinking of them lovingly. The spirits dwelling in this house may be actually *suffering* because they are aware that you are afraid of them.

DR. MONTAGUE. (*Wearily.*) We can talk about it later, my dear.

MRS. MONTAGUE. (*Coldly.*) Of course. (*Glancing at Eleanor and Theodora.*) What a pity I wasn't here when whatever it was happened. (*Luke and Arthur re-enter* U. C. *Arthur goes to Mrs. Montague's side.*)

DR. MONTAGUE. (*Turning to them.*) Thank you, gentlemen.

LUKE. Not at all. (*He crosses towards Eleanor and Theodora. With a wink.*) Golf clubs? (*The girls laugh.*)

DR. MONTAGUE. (*To Mrs. Montague and Arthur.*) Now, perhaps you'd like to freshen up before lunch. I'm sure that Mrs. Dudley has prepared something splendid for us. (*He beams, hopefully. Theodora and Eleanor are now seated on the sofa. Eleanor leans towards Theodora.*)

ELEANOR. (*Whispering.*) I wonder how long she's going to stay.

THEODORA. (*Whispering back.*) Maybe her suitcase is filled with ectoplasm. (*Mrs. Montague turns and glares at them.*)

MRS. MONTAGUE. (*Imperiously.*) What was that?

DR. MONTAGUE. (*Quickly.*) They wondered how long you can be with us. The longer the better, of course.

MRS. MONTAGUE. (*Turning to him.*) You *know* that Arthur

has to get back to his school. (*To the others.*) Arthur is a head-master. (*Arthur beams.*) He has generously cancelled his appointments for Monday, so we'll leave that afternoon. Then Arthur can be back for classes on Tuesday.

THEODORA. (*Unhappily.*) But today is only Saturday.

DR. MONTAGUE. (*Energetically.*) Isn't that fortunate? That gives us better than two full days together. *Now*, shouldn't we think about lunch?

ARTHUR. I hope the food is plain. I'm a meat and potatoes man, myself. Don't drink, don't smoke, don't read trash. Bad example for the boys at school. They look up to one a bit, you know.

THEODORA. (*Innocently.*) I'm sure they must all model themselves on you.

ARTHUR. (*Seriously.*) Get a bad sort now and then. No taste for sports, you know. Moping in corners. Crybabies. We knock *that* out of them fast enough.

LUKE. (*Leading him on.*) Toughen 'em up.

ARTHUR. *Exactly.*

MRS. MONTAGUE. Come Arthur, there'll be time for chit chat later. We'd better begin our preparations if we expect to be ready for tonight's work. (*She steps* U. C.)

DR. MONTAGUE. And just what do you have in mind for to-night?

MRS. MONTAGUE. (*Impatiently.*) I realize that *you* would never dream of going about these things with any system, but you'll have to admit, John, that in this area I have simply more of an instinctive understanding. Women do, you know. (*Glancing at Eleanor and Theodora.*) At least *some* women.

DR. MONTAGUE. My dear . . .

MRS. MONTAGUE. Therefore I have set up a definite plan of action. Tonight Arthur will patrol. I brought him along for that purpose. I will recline in your haunted room with only a night light burning, and will endeavor to get in touch with the elements disturbing this house. I *never* sleep when there are troubled spirits about.

ARTHUR. Got to go about these things in the right way. Never pays to aim low. Tell my fellows that.

MRS. MONTAGUE. And I think perhaps that after lunch we will have a little session with planchette. Just Arthur and myself, of course. The rest of you, I can see, are not ready yet; you would drive away the spirits. We will need a quiet room.

LUKE. (*Politely.*) The library, perhaps? It's one of the gloomier rooms. Might be teeming with spirits.

MRS. MONTAGUE. It should do. Books are frequently very good carriers, you know. I hope the room has been well dusted? Arthur sometimes sneezes.

DR. MONTAGUE. Mrs. Dudley keeps the entire house in perfect order.

MRS. MONTAGUE. The library it is then. And after the session I shall require a glass of milk and perhaps a small cake. Crackers will do if they are not too heavily salted.

DR. MONTAGUE. (*Wearily.*) As you wish, my dear. Now I'll show you to your rooms.

MRS. MONTAGUE. (*At the doorway,* U. C.) No need, thank you. Come Arthur. We have much to do. (*She and Arthur exit. Dr. Montague holds the door for them.*)

THEODORA. (*Confidentially, to Eleanor.*) I think I'm going to be simply crazy about Mrs. Montague.

ELEANOR. I don't know, Arthur is rather more to my taste. (*Dr. Montague steps* D. *Luke turns to him.*)

LUKE. Please, sir, *who* is planchette?

DR. MONTAGUE. (*Muttering irritably.*) The imbeciles. I hope they don't upset *everything* with their silly tampering. (*He responds to Luke's question.*) Planchette? It's a device similar to the Ouija board. A kind of spirit writing. My wife believes it to be a way to communicate with—ah—intangible beings—although to my way of thinking the only intangible beings who ever get in touch through those things are in the imaginations of the people running them. Spirit writing indeed! *Balderdash!*

THEODORA. Superstition!

ELEANOR. (*Perking up.*) What would the fellows at school think?

THEODORA. (*Looking at Eleanor. Brightly.*) Nell, dear. You suddenly look *so* much better.

LUKE. Positively radiant.

ELEANOR. (*Rising.*) And I'm *starved*. It *must* be almost time for lunch.

DR. MONTAGUE. Ah! The powers of Hill House are at work again. The storm cloud has passed. Shall we adjourn to the dining room?

49

THEODORA. (*Rising.*) I can't wait. Let's eat it *all* before Arthur and Mrs. M. come down.

LUKE. (*Chuckling.*) You devil! You'll have to fight me for it.

ELEANOR. *And* me. (*They cross* U. C. *towards the doorway.*)

DR. MONTAGUE. (*Paternally.*) My children. My children are back with me again. (*He turns and follows them out* U. C., *shaking his head, as*)

THE CURTAIN FALLS

ACT TWO

Scene Two

That evening. Again the action and lighting are confined to the parlor area. Dr. Montague and Luke are at the chess table, D. R., *engrossed in their game. Eleanor sits in one of the* D. L. *chairs, reading, while Theodora is curled up on the sofa looking through Hugh Crain's "scrapbook." Dr. Montague ponders a move and then, after making it, looks up hopefully at his opponent. Luke grimaces, hesitates, and then makes a countermove. Dr. Montague studies Luke's action, after which his face falls. The* U. C. *doors open and Mrs. Montague enters, followed by Arthur.*

MRS. MONTAGUE. (*Effusively.*) Planchette has been *very* kind tonight. (*She crosses to Dr. Montague.*) John, there are definitely foreign elements present in this house.

DR. MONTAGUE. (*Drily.*) You don't say.

ARTHUR. (*To Eleanor and Theodora.*) Quite a splendid sitting, really. (*He waves a sheaf of papers at them.*) Very tangible results.

MRS. MONTAGUE. We've gotten a good deal of information for you. (*Dr. Montague studies the chess board.*) John!

DR. MONTAGUE. (*Looking up.*) Yes, my dear. (*She glowers.*) I was listening, I assure you.

MRS. MONTAGUE. I hope so . . . Now. Planchette was quite insistent about a nun. Have you learned anything about a nun, John? (*Turning to the others.*) Have any of you?

50

LUKE. A nun? In Hill House? Not likely.

MRS. MONTAGUE. Planchette felt very strongly about a nun. Perhaps something of the sort—a dark, vague figure even—has been seen in or near the house? Or appeared to the villagers at night and frightened them?

DR. MONTAGUE. (*Shrugging.*) The figure of a nun is fairly common—

MRS. MONTAGUE. (*Brusquely.*) John, *if* you please. I assume you are suggesting that I am mistaken—or that *planchette* is mistaken. I assure you this is not the case. A nun was most specifically suggested.

DR. MONTAGUE. (*Reasonably.*) I am only trying to say, my dear, that the spectre of a nun is far and away the most common form of appearance. There has never been such a thing connected with Hill House.

MRS. MONTAGUE. (*Icily.*) John, *if* you *please*. May I continue? Or is planchette to be dismissed without a hearing? (*Dr. Montague shrugs again.*) Thank you . . . Now then. There is also a name, spelled variously as Helen, or Helene, or Elena. Who might that be?

DR. MONTAGUE. My dear, many people have lived in this—

MRS. MONTAGUE. (*Going on, firmly.*) *Helen* brought us a warning against a mysterious monk. Now when a monk and a nun *both* turn up in one house—

ARTHUR. (*Sitting in chair beside Eleanor's.*) Expect the place was built on an older site. Previous influences prevailing, you know.

MRS. MONTAGUE. (*To Arthur.*) It sounds very much like broken vows to me. *Very* much.

ARTHUR. Had a lot of that back then, you know. Temptation, probably.

DR. MONTAGUE. I hardly think—

MRS. MONTAGUE. (*Ignoring him.*) I daresay she was walled up alive. The nun, I mean. They always did that. (*To the girls, who have been listening politely.*) You've no idea the messages I've gotten from nuns walled up alive.

DR. MONTAGUE. There is *no* case on record of *any* nun *ever* being—

MRS. MONTAGUE. (*To her husband.*) May I point out once more that I *myself* have received messages from such nuns? Or is it possible that I am mistaken again, John?

51

DR. MONTAGUE. (*Wearily.*) Certainly not, my dear. (*He glances at Luke.*) I concede. It's your game. (*He rises.*)

LUKE. (*Pleasantly.*) You're a worthy opponent, Doctor. Shall we have another go at it later?

DR. MONTAGUE. As you wish. (*Luke lines up the chessmen.*)

ARTHUR. They usually put them away with one candle and a crust of bread. Horrible thing to do, when you think about it.

DR. MONTAGUE. (*Crossing* u.) No nun was *ever* walled up alive. It's all legend. Imagination.

MRS. MONTAGUE. (*Following him.*) All right, John. We won't quarrel over it. Just understand, however, that sometimes purely materialistic views give way before *facts.* Now it is a proven fact that among the visitations troubling this house are a nun and also . . . (*She pauses, waiting for someone to react.*)

LUKE. (*Quickly.*) What else was there? (*Mrs. Montague turns.*) I am *so* interested in hearing what—ah—planchette had to say.

MRS. MONTAGUE. (*Waggling a finger at Luke.*) Nothing about *you,* young man. (*Coyly.*) Although one of the young ladies present may hear something of interest. (*Eleanor and Theodora glance at her. Mrs. Montague looks mysterious.*) Oh, yes— Helen wants us to search the cellar for an old well.

LUKE. You think Helen was buried alive?

MRS. MONTAGUE. I doubt it. More likely we'll find evidence of the missing nun.

DR. MONTAGUE. More likely we'll find eighty years of rubbish.

MRS. MONTAGUE. (*Turning.*) John, I *cannot* understand this skepticism in you, of all people. After all you *did* come to this house to collect evidence of supernatural activity. But now, when I bring you a full account of the *causes*—and an indication of where to start looking—you are positively scornful.

DR. MONTAGUE. We have no authority to dig up the cellar.

MRS. MONTAGUE. (*Hopefully.*) Arthur could—

DR. MONTAGUE. (*Breaking in, firmly.*) No. My lease specifically forbids any tampering. We are students—not vandals.

MRS. MONTAGUE. (*Innocently.*) I should think you'd want to know the truth, John.

DR. MONTAGUE. (*Stepping away from her.*) There is *nothing* I should like to know more.

MRS. MONTAGUE. (*Sighing.*) Dear me, how patient one must be sometimes. (*She shakes her head.*) But I do want to read you the little passage we received toward the end. (*She crosses to Arthur.*) Arthur, do you have it? (*Arthur shuffles through his papers.*) It was just after the message about the flowers you are to send to your sick aunt. (*She beams at Eleanor and Theodora.*) Planchette has a control named Merrigot who's taken a genuine personal interest in Arthur. Brings him word from distant relatives, and so on.

THEODORA. (*With a glance at Eleanor.*) How nice.

ARTHUR. (*Gravely.*) She's not seriously ill, you understand. Merrigot was most reassuring.

MRS. MONTAGUE. (*Leaning over Arthur's shoulder and running her finger down the page.*) Here it is. Arthur, you read the questions and I'll read the answers.

ARTHUR. (*Brightly.*) Off we go. (*Studying the page.*) Now— let me see—start right about here?

MRS. MONTAGUE. With "Who are you?"

ARTHUR. Check. (*He clears his throat.*) "Who are you?"

MRS. MONTAGUE. (*Reading.*) "Nell." (*The others turn and listen. Eleanor frowns.*)

ELEANOR. (*Interrupting.*) Nell who?

MRS. MONTAGUE. (*Casually.*) Eleanor Nellie Nell Nell. They sometimes do that. Repeat a word over and over to make sure it comes across all right. (*Eleanor appears unsatisfied by the answer. Mrs. Montague nudges Arthur to continue.*) Go on.

ARTHUR. (*Reading.*) "What do you want?"

MRS. MONTAGUE. (*Reading.*) "Home."

ARTHUR. (*Reading.*) "Do you want to go home?" (*Theodora glances at Eleanor, who looks away. Luke and Dr. Montague listen attentively.*)

MRS. MONTAGUE. (*Reading.*) "Want to be home."

ARTHUR. (*Reading.*) "What are you doing here?"

MRS. MONTAGUE. (*Reading.*) "Waiting."

ARTHUR. (*Reading.*) "Waiting for what?"

MRS. MONTAGUE. (*Reading.*) "Home."

ARTHUR. (*Looking up.*) There it is again. If they like a word they use it over and over, just for the sound of it.

MRS. MONTAGUE. Ordinarily we never ask *why.* It tends to confuse planchette. But this time we were bold, and came right out with it. (*She taps Arthur on the shoulder.*) Arthur?

ARTHUR. (*Reading.*) "Why?"

MRS. MONTAGUE. (*Reading.*) "Mother."

ARTHUR. (*Reading.*) "Is Hill House your home?"

MRS. MONTAGUE. (*Reading.*) "Home." (*Dr. Montague sighs.*)

ARTHUR. (*Reading.*) "Are you suffering?"

MRS. MONTAGUE. (*Shaking her head.*) No answer here. Sometimes they dislike admitting to pain.

ARTHUR. (*Glancing up at the others.*) Stoical. (*Reading.*) "Can we help you?"

MRS. MONTAGUE. (*Reading.*) "No. Lost. Lost. Lost." (*She looks up.*) You see? One word repeated again. I've had one word go on to cover a whole page sometimes.

ARTHUR. (*Reading.*) "What do you want?"

MRS. MONTAGUE. (*Reading.*) "Mother."

ARTHUR. (*Reading.*) "Why?"

MRS. MONTAGUE. (*Reading.*) "Child."

ARTHUR. (*Reading.*) "Where is your mother?"

MRS. MONTAGUE. (*Reading.*) "Home."

ARTHUR. (*Reading.*) "Where is your home?"

MRS. MONTAGUE. (*Reading.*) "Lost. Lost. Lost." (*She looks up.*) After that there was nothing but gibberish. (*Dr. Montague makes a wry face.*)

ARTHUR. (*Confidentially.*) Never known planchette so cooperative. Quite an experience, really.

THEODORA. (*Annoyed. Nodding towards Eleanor.*) But why pick on Nell? Your fool planchette has no right to send messages to people without permission or—

ARTHUR. (*Defensively.*) You'll never get results by abusing planchette—

MRS. MONTAGUE. (*Turning quickly to Eleanor.*) You're Nell? (*She turns to Theodora.*) We thought you were Nell.

THEODORA. (*Flippantly.*) So?

MRS. MONTAGUE. (*Irritably.*) It doesn't affect our messages, of course, but I *do* think that we might have been correctly introduced. I am sure that planchette knew the difference between you —but I do not care to be misled.

LUKE. (*To Theodora.*) Don't feel neglected. We'll bury you alive.

THEODORA. When I get a message from that thing I want it to be about hidden treasure. None of this nonsense about sending flowers to an aunt.

ELEANOR. (*After a pause. Quietly.*) Why do you think all that was sent to me?

MRS. MONTAGUE. (*Shrugging.*) Really child, I couldn't *begin* to say. Perhaps you are more receptive psychically than you realize, although how you *could* be I don't know. All these days here without picking up the simplest message from beyond. (*Eleanor glances at Theodora, and then looks away quickly.*) The fire wants stirring.

THEODORA. Nell doesn't want messages from beyond.

LUKE. (*Kindly.*) Nell wants her warm bed and a little sleep.

DR. MONTAGUE. And perhaps a spot of brandy first? What say we all have one? (*Theodora nods affirmatively.*)

LUKE. Fine idea. (*He rises and crosses* u. *towards the sideboard.*) May I?

MRS. MONTAGUE. (*To Luke.*) None for us, thanks. We must keep clear heads tonight. Arthur, we'd best be on our way.

ARTHUR. (*Rising. Looking pleased.*) Righto.

MRS. MONTAGUE. (*Turning to the others.*) Arthur will patrol the house. Every hour, regularly, he will make a round of the upstairs rooms.

ARTHUR. (*Very serious.*) I shall have a drawn revolver, a flashlight and a loud whistle, in case I should observe anything worth your notice, or require . . . ah . . . company. You may all sleep quietly, I assure you. I'm an excellent shot.

MRS. MONTAGUE. And 7 shall be in the nursery. Awake. (*Lyrically.*) It is *such* a blessing to know that the beings in this house are only waiting for an opportunity to tell their stories and free themselves from the burden of their sorrow. (*To Arthur.*) Shall we go?

DR. MONTAGUE. (*Stepping towards her.*) My dear, are you sure . . . ? I wonder whether you ought to have someone with you. (*During this Luke fills four brandy glasses and places them on a tray. He serves them to Eleanor, Theodora and Dr. Montague and, after taking the fourth glass himself, puts the tray back on the sideboard.*)

MRS. MONTAGUE. (*Amused.*) Really, John. How many, many hours have I sat in a room with those who have passed beyond? How can I make you perceive that there is no danger where there is nothing but love and sympathetic understanding? I am here to *help* these unfortunate beings.

DR. MONTAGUE. (*Not convinced.*) I know. But leave your door
open, just in case.

MRS. MONTAGUE. (*Agreeably.*) Unlocked, if you insist.

DR. MONTAGUE. And I shall be right down the hall. If you
need anything I can hear you.

MRS. MONTAGUE. (*With a laugh, as she turns* U.) These others
need your protection so much more than I. They are so *very*
vulnerable, with their hard hearts and unseeing eyes. (*She opens
the* U. C. *doors. Arthur is behind her.*)

DR. MONTAGUE. Be careful, all the same. Good night.

MRS. MONTAGUE. Good night. (*She smiles at the others.*)
Please don't be afraid. No matter what happens, remember—*I* am
here. (*She exits, followed by Arthur.*)

ELEANOR. (*Absently.*) Good night. (*Luke nods.*)

THEODORA. (*After her.*) Good night. Happy hunting.

LUKE. (*Raising his glass.*) To all the poor unfortunates in the
afterworld. May they congregate tonight in the nursery. (*Theodora
laughs. They all drink.*)

THEODORA. I swear she's going to blow this house wide open
with that perfect love business. If ever I saw a place that had no
use for perfect love, it's Hill House.

LUKE. Having Arthur prowling about with a loaded revolver
doesn't make me any happier, either. He's apt to shoot somebody.

DR. MONTAGUE. (*Darkly.*) I don't like it. We'd better stay
here together for awhile. Something's going to happen. I don't like
it.

THEODORA. I hope she hasn't gone and made anything mad with
her planchette.

DR. MONTAGUE. (*Shaking his head.*) She is really a good wife,
and an excellent woman in most respects. (*He gestures off* U.)
This is practically her only vice.

ELEANOR. Perhaps she feels she is helping you with your work.
(*Dr. Montague shrugs, and sips his brandy. A door slams loudly
somewhere deep in the house. Dr. Montague stiffens and signals
for silence. The others exchange apprehensive glances. The sound
of a rising wind builds offstage as though it were blowing through
the hall beyond the* U. C. *doors.*)

DR. MONTAGUE. Steady, now. Be calm. (*He crosses* U. C. *and
puts his hand on the doorknob, listening. Eleanor shivers, and joins
Theodora on the sofa. They sit close to each other. Luke crosses*

u. *and stands by Dr. Montague. The noise of the wind grows
louder, but, through it, can be heard the sound of doors being
knocked on.)*
ELEANOR. *(In a small voice.)* It's so cold. It's coming again.
(Theodora puts her arm around her. The knocking comes closer.)
LUKE. *(Hands in pockets against the cold.)* It's nowhere near the
nursery, that's for sure.
THEODORA. *Really.* Next summer I must go somewhere else.
LUKE. *(Turning.)* There are disadvantages everywhere. In the
mountains you get mosquitoes.
DR. MONTAGUE. *(Anxiously.)* I'm going to have to go out
there. She might be frightened.
LUKE. *(Putting his hand out to stop the doctor from opening the
door.)* It never hurt *us.* It won't hurt *them.*
DR. MONTAGUE. *(Grimly, taking his hand from the doorknob.)*
I only hope she doesn't try to *do* anything about it. *(The pound-
ing grows louder and closer.)*
THEODORA. I feel like an old hand at this. *(To Eleanor.)* Warm
enough? *(Eleanor nods. Suddenly there is silence. They look at
each other anxiously.)*
LUKE. *(Trying to disguise his nervousness.)* More brandy, anyone? My passion for spirits—
THEODORA. *(Wildly.)* Oh lord! Not *that* pun!
LUKE. *(Stepping to the sideboard.)* Sorry . . . but I no longer
think of it as a pun. *(He crosses to the sofa with the brandy decanter, and fills the girls' glasses.)*
THEODORA. *(To Eleanor.)* Here. Drink. *(They sip their brandy.
Luke crosses back to the sideboard, fills his own glass, and raises
it to drink as the pounding begins again—directly on the* u. c.
doors. Luke puts his glass down quickly, steps l., *and pulls the
doctor. away from the doors. The hinges of the doors strain and
heave under the pounding. Theodora chants in a low voice.)* It
can't get in, it can't get in. *(She looks over at the doctor and Luke,
who stand tense and helpless.)* Don't let it get in. *(Suddenly the
pounding stops and the doorknob begins to turn—slowly at first,
and then violently.)*
ELEANOR. It knows we're here. *(Luke turns and gestures furi-
ously for her to be quiet. She shivers, and they hear little patting
sounds around the doorframe.)*
THEODORA. *(Giggling.)* Purest love. Purest love.

57

LUKE. (*Nervously.*) I hope they've closed their doors . . . (*Outside the door there is a murmuring sound, and then the roar of wind rises again, as though it were racing up and down the hall. There is a tapping on the door and Luke puts his shoulder against it. He looks back at the girls, who are huddled on the sofa.*) Are you all right? Theo, are you all right?

THEODORA. Hanging on. (*She glances at Eleanor, who huddles in silence.*) I don't know about Nell.

DR. MONTAGUE. (*To both of them.*) Keep warm. We haven't seen it all yet. (*Suddenly the pounding begins again, directly on the doors and even louder and more violent than before. There is wild laughter from beyond, u. c., as Luke and Dr. Montague press against the doors, and Theodora and Eleanor cling together in fright. The lights go down slowly as the sounds of roaring wind, laughter and pounding build to an enormous, echoing crescendo. Then silence. After a long pause, Eleanor's voice comes out of the darkness.*)

ELEANOR. (*In a level voice.*) I'll come. If that's what you want. Tell me where and how. I'll come. (*Again silence, and then the lights begin to come up slowly. Luke and Dr. Montague, both disheveled, rush D. to the sofa, where Theodora bends over Eleanor.*)

THEODORA. (*Rubbing Eleanor's hands.*) She's all right, I think. (*They peer at Eleanor anxiously. She sits up and shakes her head, as though coming to consciousness.*)

ELEANOR. (*Blinking.*) How . . . what?

DR. MONTAGUE. (*Bending over her.*) How are you, my dear?

ELEANOR. What happened?

DR. MONTAGUE. It was just another . . . night. But I sense that perhaps you've had enough of it. In the morning—

ELEANOR. (*Quickly.*) No, no. I'm fine. Honestly I am. Are the others . . . all right?

DR. MONTAGUE. They're perfectly safe, I'm sure. I can't believe that my wife stirred up that storm—but one more word about pure love . . .

ELEANOR. But what happened?

THEODORA. (*Lightly.*) Hill House went dancing, taking us along on a mad, midnight fling.

LUKE. Turning somersaults as it went.

ELEANOR. I don't seem to remember . . . (*Firmly.*) And yet I *wasn't* really afraid. I *know* I wasn't.

DR. MONTAGUE. (*Thoughtfully.*) No, my dear. I don't think you were. (*Disturbed.*) But I wish it wasn't so.

ELEANOR. (*Flustered.*) But, I . . .

DR. MONTAGUE. (*Glancing at his watch.*) Now, it's quite late. When you're ready . . .

THEODORA. (*Standing up and pulling Eleanor to her feet.*) Come along, baby. Theo will wash your face and help you get settled for a good night's sleep. Uninterrupted, I hope.

LUKE. For all of us. With dear Arthur standing guard.

THEODORA. Amen. (*They start* u.)

DR. MONTAGUE. And looking for activity in the wrong places. (*The others turn and regard him quizzically.*) I mean . . . I don't believe that Mrs. Montague and Arthur heard *any* of this. I don't think that they have the slightest idea of what went on. (*Pause.*) Hill House didn't mean it for them. (*Their faces reflecting doubt and uncertainty, the others ponder the doctor's words for a moment, and then turn slowly* u., *as*)

THE CURTAIN FALLS

ACT THREE

SCENE ONE

The next evening. As the curtain rises the parlor area is illuminated, but empty. After a moment the u. c. doors open and Eleanor and Theodora enter, followed by Luke and Dr. Montague. Theodora steps L. to the desk and drops a sheaf of notes. The others go by her into the room.

THEODORA. (*To the others.*) I hate writing these notes. I feel like a darn fool trying to describe everything, without sounding weird myself.

DR. MONTAGUE. It's all in a good cause, my dear. *Think* of the stir my book will make in scientific circles.

LUKE. I wonder what this mysterious book will be like? (*To Dr. Montague.*) Will we all be in it?

DR. MONTAGUE. Of course. You will turn up as earnest young psychic researchers.

LUKE. Ah! (*They cross D. Eleanor sits in one of the chairs at L.*)

THEODORA. But these post-dinner sessions in the dining room! It's like study hall! (*She sits in the other L. chair.*)

DR. MONTAGUE. How else can I keep my chickens together?

ELEANOR. (*Taunting.*) And on a faintly serious track?

THEODORA. (*In mock despair.*) Oh dear. Nell is displeased again. It's your fault, Luke. You're entirely too frivolous and silly.

LUKE. (*With a smile.*) I shall try to reform.

ELEANOR. (*Nestling into her chair.*) Oh, for heaven's sake. (*Dr. Montague crosses to the chess table, D. R., and sets up the pieces for a game.*)

LUKE. No, I *mean* it. After all, Hill House *will* be mine someday, with all its untold treasures and secrets. I'll never make a proper lord of the manor unless I learn to be more serious—or perhaps I should say sinister.

THEODORA. Sinister, by all means, if you're going to fit in around here.

ELEANOR. (*Teasing him.*) What about your career as a bull-fighter? Would you give that up for Hill House?

LUKE. (*Quite serious.*) I think one would be good training for the other. It helps to be fearless, living in a house like this.

THEODORA. And if you shouldn't survive, Nell would be glad to look after Hill House for you, wouldn't you, Nell? (*Eleanor glances at her questioningly. To Luke.*) She'd like to stay here and write on the walls.

ELEANOR. (*Looking away.*) That's over and forgotten, Theo.

THEODORA. Actually, I can't understand *anyone* wanting to own this place. Far too gloomy, if you ask me.

LUKE. Granted. But intriguing, too. Fact is, you never really know what you are going to want until you suddenly see it clearly. If I never had a chance of owning Hill House I might feel differently. But now . . .

THEODORA. I predict a lonely life. This is hardly the sort of threshold to carry a bride over.

LUKE. (*Shrugging.*) Oh well, what do people really want with other people, anyway? What use are other people? (*He glances over at Dr. Montague.*) A game, Doctor? I feel infallible tonight.

DR. MONTAGUE. (*Smiling.*) I'll risk it.

LUKE. There's no risk—as you'll see. (*To Theodora and Eleanor.*) If you'll excuse me, ladies. (*They nod. Luke crosses to the chess table and sits opposite Dr. Montague. They are quickly engrossed in their game.*)

THEODORA. (*To Eleanor.*) What use are other people, indeed!

ELEANOR. (*Thoughtfully.*) I sometimes wonder, myself. (*Pause, then gravely.*) It was my fault my mother died. I'm more sure of it all the time. She knocked on the wall and called me and called me and I never woke up. I ought to have brought her the medicine, I always did before. But this time she called me and I never woke up.

THEODORA. All that should be over and forgotten, too.

ELEANOR. (*Ignoring her.*) I've wondered ever since if I did wake up. If I woke up and heard her—and just went back to sleep. It would have been so easy to do. I've wondered about it.

THEODORA. You worry too much, Nell. You probably *like* thinking it was your fault.

61

ELEANOR. It was going to happen sooner or later, in any case. And it was *sure* to be my fault, no matter what.

THEODORA. If it hadn't happened you would never have come to Hill House.

ELEANOR. (*Seriously.*) I'd have regretted that. But I still don't know what happens next.

THEODORA. Why, back to your cozy little apartment, what else?

ELEANOR. (*Shaking her head.*) No.

THEODORA. Well?

ELEANOR. (*Quietly.*) I'm coming with you.

THEODORA. (*Surprised.*) Coming *where* with me?

ELEANOR. Back with you, back home. I'm going to follow you home.

THEODORA. (*Blankly.*) Why?

ELEANOR. I never had anyone to care about, except Mother. I want to be someplace where I belong.

THEODORA. (*Lightly.*) I'm not in the habit of taking home stray cats.

ELEANOR. (*Smiling.*) I *am* a kind of stray cat, aren't I?

THEODORA. (*Patting her arm.*) You have your own home. You'll be glad enough to get back to it when the time comes. We'll all be glad to get home again.

ELEANOR. (*In a level voice.*) I'll come, you know. I will.

THEODORA. (*Suddenly concerned that Eleanor means what she says. She rises.*) Nell, dear. You have your life, I have mine. We'll write each other, of course. But Hill House isn't forever, you know.

ELEANOR. I can get a job. I won't be in your way.

THEODORA. (*Turning to her.*) I don't understand. (*With a touch of acid.*) Do you *always* go where you're not wanted?

ELEANOR. (*Undaunted. Smiling.*) I've never *been* wanted anywhere. Perhaps that's the problem. (*Theodora looks puzzled and annoyed.*)

DR. MONTAGUE. (*Looking up from the chess game.*) May I suggest that a good night's sleep might be in order? I think we're all a bit tired after last night.

THEODORA. I know *I* am. Too tired to squabble over ridiculous things.

ELEANOR. I'm serious, Theo.

THEODORA. (*Crossing R. to the chess table.*) Well, so am I. And

I don't want to talk about it any more. (*She turns her attention to the chess game.*)

ELEANOR. (*After a pause.*) I'm sorry. Forgive me? (*Theodora looks at her for a moment.*)

THEODORA. (*Firmly.*) No more talk. Promise?

ELEANOR. (*Nodding.*) Promise. We can settle it in the morning.

THEODORA. (*Exasperated.*) Good lord! You *are* a pest. (*She turns back to the chess game. Luke and Dr. Montague smile to themselves.*)

ELEANOR. (*Quietly.*) Never make decisions in anger, Theo. (*Theodora looks at her thoughtfully for a moment, and then back at the game. Suddenly the u. c. doors open and Mrs. Montague storms in, followed by Arthur. She crosses to the chess table, and breaks in abruptly.*)

MRS. MONTAGUE. I must say, I really must *say*—this is the most *infuriating* . . .

DR. MONTAGUE. (*Looking up, puzzled.*) My dear . . .

MRS. MONTAGUE. (*Raging on.*) If you had the *decency*, the common *decency*. After all, John, I *did* come all this way, and so did Arthur, just to help out, and I certainly must say that I never expected to meet with such cynicism and incredulity from *you*, of all people, and *these* . . . (*She gestures at Luke and the girls.*) All I ask, all I *ask*, is some small minimum of trust, just a little bit of sympathy for all I'm trying to do. And instead, you disbelieve, you scoff, you mock, you jeer.

DR. MONTAGUE. (*Bewildered.*) Whatever is the matter . . . ?

MRS. MONTAGUE. (*Wagging a finger at her husband. Bitterly.*) Planchette will not speak to me tonight. Not *one single word* have I had from planchette, as a direct result of your sneering and skepticism. It may be silent for weeks, thanks to you. The very *least* I expected was a little respect. (*Luke covers a smile.*)

DR. MONTAGUE. (*Reasonably.*) My dear, I am certain that none of us has knowingly interfered.

MRS. MONTAGUE. Mocking and jeering, were you not? Planchette knows. (*She turns to the others.*) And these young people, pert and insolent?

LUKE. Mrs. Montague, really . . . (*She turns away in silent fury. Theodora sighs, and crosses u.*)

ARTHUR. (*Confidentially.*) Never seen her so upset, you know.

Miserable experience, waiting for planchette. So easily offended, of course. Sensitive to atmosphere.

MRS. MONTAGUE. (*Turning back.*) It's simply that it's a most delicate and intricate piece of machinery. The slightest air of disbelief offends it. (*Looking at the others accusingly.*) How would you feel if people refused to believe in *you*?

THEODORA. (*At the* u. c. *doors.*) I don't know—but I'm too sleepy to figure it out now. I'm going to bed. I'll think beautiful thoughts about planchette as I drift off. Would that help?

MRS. MONTAGUE. Humph! (*She sits on the sofa, looking away angrily.*)

THEODORA. Coming, Nell? I don't want to go upstairs alone, even filled with purest love as I am. (*Mrs. Montague glowers.*)

ELEANOR. (*Rising and stretching.*) I'm with you. (*She crosses* u. c.) Good night, all.

DR. MONTAGUE. Goodnight, sleep tight.

LUKE. Goodnight, sweet ladies. (*They exit.*)

MRS. MONTAGUE. (*After they have gone.*) They can rest, of course. They don't feel the urgency which I do. But *why* must they scoff?

DR. MONTAGUE. Really, my dear. I think you exaggerate. (*Mrs. Montague fumes.*)

ARTHUR. (*Rambling on. A smile plays on Luke's face as he listens.*) I don't know how they can get much sleep, actually. Food's so rich around here. Keeps you awake. If I had my way there'd be no more fancy sauces. Teach my fellows it's the mark of a cad. Fancy food and women waiting on you. *My* fellows wait on themselves. Mark of a man.

LUKE. (*To Arthur.*) And what else do you teach them?

ARTHUR. Teach? You mean like algebra, Latin? Leave all that kind of thing to the masters.

LUKE. How many fellows are there in your school?

ARTHUR. How many? Got a crack tennis team, you know. Absolutely tophole. (*He looks questioningly at Luke.*) Not counting milksops?

LUKE. (*Agreeably.*) Not counting milksops.

ARTHUR. Oh, Tennis. Golf. Baseball. Track. Cricket. (*He smiles slyly.*) Didn't guess we played cricket, did you? Then there's swimming and volley ball. Some fellows go out for everything, though. All-around types. (*Mrs. Montague shows signs of im-patience.*) Maybe seventy, altogether.

MRS. MONTAGUE. (*Abruptly.*) Arthur? That's enough shop talk now. We've got other matters which need our attention.

ARTHUR. (*Attentively.*) Yes, of course. Silly of me. Get to rambling on about school. (*Dr. Montague and Luke resume their game.*)

MRS. MONTAGUE. (*With resolution.*) I won't let the taunts of unbelievers discourage me, I *won't*. The poor souls wandering restlessly here *need* my understanding and love. (*Magnanimously.*) I shall not stop trying to come to their aid. (*She rises.*)

ARTHUR. (*Eagerly.*) You mean, another go at planchette? (*With admiration.*) Despite all?

MRS. MONTAGUE. (*Her lips set.*) Precisely.

DR. MONTAGUE. (*Looking up from his game.*) I don't think . . .

MRS. MONTAGUE. (*Sharply.*) I *do* think. (*She crosses u.*) I owe it to *them* not to let you defeat me. Come, Arthur. Perhaps we've cleared the air a bit.

ARTHUR. (*Getting up and following her.*) That's the spirit. (*Turning back.*) Can't understand you fellows, getting all nervy about this place. Sat up last night with my revolver and not a mouse stirred. Only sound was a branch tapping on the window. (*He holds the u. c. doors for Mrs. Montague.*) Nearly drove me crazy. (*Luke and Dr. Montague exchange glances.*)

MRS. MONTAGUE. (*Coldly.*) We'll be in the library, if anyone cares. (*She sweeps out, as Dr. Montague sighs. Arthur follows her. Dr. Montague looks back at Luke and shrugs.*)

DR. MONTAGUE. (*Shaking his head.*) Absolute rubbish, the whole business. But harmless, I'm sure. If I thought otherwise I'd send her home tomorrow, and that nincompoop with her. Milksops, if you please!

LUKE. (*Moving a chess piece.*) Checkmate.

DR. MONTAGUE. (*Coming back to the matter at hand.*) Yes. What? (*He looks at the board and scowls. He snaps his fingers in disappointment.*) You won't get away with that again, I promise you. Not if we have to sit here all night. (*He concentrates on the game, chin in hands, as the lights gradually come down in the parlor area. After a few moments of total darkness, during which Dr. Montague and Luke exit unseen, the light on the bureau in Eleanor's room comes up slowly. She is in bed, asleep. She begins* to toss about, moaning to herself. She rolls over on her back, and pulls the covers close under her chin. Her eyes are still closed.)

ELEANOR. (In her sleep, indistinctly.) Mother? Mother? Where? (She lies quietly a moment, then opens her eyes and sits up. She speaks in a level voice.) Mother? (She looks around her.) You're here somewhere. Aren't you, Mother? (From off U. comes a soft, low moan. Eleanor sits bolt upright, frozen in attention. She listens closely, and then a smile crosses her face. She throws the bed clothes aside, and sits on the edge of the bed.) I'll come, Mother. I do hear you . . . this time. (The moan is repeated. Eleanor gets up and goes to the U. R. door and listens a moment.) Are you out there? Tell me where. (Quietly she opens the door and looks out. Then she exits. The lights go down in her room. After a suitable pause the house lights come up dimly in the now empty parlor area. The U. C. doors open quietly, and Eleanor tiptoes in. She stops below the doors and looks about her questioningly.) In here? Is this where you are? (She listens.) I want to come, Mother. (She listens again and then suddenly, laughing gaily, she begins to twirl about like a dancer, her nightgown billowing around her. She pirouettes towards R., singing to herself, then stops as abruptly as she began when laughter is heard from off L. It is again a tinkling, disembodied laugh, running quickly up the scale and then stopping with a little gasp. Eleanor turns quickly, craning to hear. Then she crosses slowly L.) Mother. Mother, dear. I'm sorry for what happened and I won't leave you again, I promise. (She reaches the L. wall and stops, listening attentively. The laugh comes again, and this time Eleanor turns her head quickly towards the tower in the U. L. wall. She goes to it and puts her hand on the doorknob, turning it slowly. The door opens. Eleanor stiffens.) In here? The tower? Please answer. (She smiles.) Oh yes. I do want to come. I belong here now. (She steps into the tower. The stage is empty for a long moment. Then voices are heard in the hall calling "Eleanor," and the U. C. doors open again. Dr. Montague rushes in, flashlight in hand, followed by Luke and Theodora, all in their bathrobes. They quickly turn on the lights, and look about the room.)

THEODORA. Eleanor? (She notices the tower door ajar.) Dr. Montague. (He turns to her. She points L. He glances at the door, then moves to it quickly, flashing his light inside and up. Theodora hangs back a moment. To Luke.) It's never been unlocked before.

66

(*Worried.*) I don't like it. (*Luke looks at her warily and then crosses to join Dr. Montague.*)

DR. MONTAGUE. (*Turning back to them.*) She's in there. On the stairs. We must be careful not to frighten her. She could fall. (*Luke takes the doctor's flashlight and peers inside.*)

LUKE. (*Withdrawing.*) The stairs have rotted away from the wall. (*Theodora gasps.*)

DR. MONTAGUE. (*He takes back the flashlight and looks inside again. He calls up.*) Eleanor? Can you hear me? (*Pause.*) Turn around very carefully and come slowly down the steps. Move very, very slowly, Eleanor. Hold onto the railing all the time. Do you understand? (*Pause.*) Now turn and come down. (*He peers up into the tower, then withdraws and whispers to the others.*) She heard me. She's coming. (*Suddenly there is an ominous cracking sound, and a muffled scream from above. Dr. Montague quickly looks into the tower again, flashing his light up inside.*) Hold still, Eleanor. Don't move. (*As he speaks the u. c. doors open again and Mrs. Montague and Arthur rush in, also dressed for bed. Arthur holds his revolver at the ready. They cross quickly to the others.*)

MRS. MONTAGUE. What on earth is going on here? You woke us up with your shouting.

THEODORA. (*Signalling her to silence.*) It's Eleanor. She's in the tower.

MRS. MONTAGUE. (*Annoyed.*) Whatever for? Make her come down so we can go back to bed. Arthur, make her come down at once. (*Arthur steps towards the tower door, but Luke blocks his way.*)

ARTHUR. (*Drawing back.*) See here . . .

LUKE. (*In a level voice.*) You stay where you are. And put that gun away, for God's sake! (*He turns to Dr. Montague.*) I'd better get her down. I think I weigh less than you do.

DR. MONTAGUE. (*Handing him the flashlight.*) Be careful, my boy. The stairs may not hold both of you.

MRS. MONTAGUE. (*Pushing past the others and looking up into the tower.*) Of course they won't. You'll have the whole thing down on our heads. (*Luke steps by her and enters the tower cautiously.*)

LUKE. (*Calling up to Eleanor.*) Eleanor, stand still. Don't move. Stay perfectly quiet. (*He disappears inside the tower. Theodora and Dr. Montague crowd into the doorway and look up after him. Mrs. Montague and Arthur are behind them.)*

THEODORA. *(Nervously.)* Nell, do as he tells you. Please.

DR. MONTAGUE. Steady, Eleanor. *Steady.*

THEODORA. That's it. Move *very* slowly. Do what Luke says. *(Pause. They peer up inside anxiously.)* Don't be frightened, Nell. You'll be all right.

DR. MONTAGUE. Only a little farther. That's it. *That's it. (The beam of the flashlight plays out of the doorway, and then Eleanor comes out, looking dazed and bewildered. Theodora puts her arm around her. Luke steps out after her. He wipes his brow with relief.)*

THEODORA. Poor Nell.

DR. MONTAGUE. *(Patting Luke on the back.)* Good job, my boy.

ELEANOR. *(Distantly.)* I ran up. I ran up all the way. She was calling me. *(She looks at Theodora questioningly.)* But I couldn't get out. The upper door was nailed shut.

LUKE. *(Behind them.)* Damn right it was. And lucky for you, too.

DR. MONTAGUE. *(In a fatherly tone of voice.)* It's all over now, my dear. You're safe with us. *(They lead Eleanor to the sofa.)* Come over here and rest a moment.

MRS. MONTAGUE. *(Petulant.)* Does anybody agree with me in thinking that this young woman has given us quite enough trouble for tonight? I, for one, would like to go back to bed, and so would Arthur.

DR. MONTAGUE. *(With forbearance.)* I don't think you quite understand. Hill House . . .

MRS. MONTAGUE. *(Breaking in.)* After this ridiculous performance Hill House will do nothing. There will be no hope of manifestations now, I can tell you. If you'll excuse me I will say goodnight. *(She snaps her head in summons.)* Arthur. *(They turn and sweep out. Dr. Montague looks after them in dismay.)*

THEODORA. *(To Dr. Montague.)* Doctor— I think Luke was scared. *(Dr. Montague turns back to the others.)*

LUKE. He most certainly was. So scared he almost didn't get himself down from there. Nell, what an imbecile you are. *(Eleanor blinks, as though coming back to normal.)*

DR. MONTAGUE. I would be inclined to agree with Luke. But thank God we got here when we did.

THEODORA. (*Compassionately, looking at Eleanor.*) I suppose you *had* to do it, Nell?

ELEANOR. (*Looking away. She has broken the spell now.*) I'm all right. I . . . I just came down to get my book. (*Sheepishly.*) Honestly I did.

DR. MONTAGUE. (*Shaking his head.*) And the tower door was open? Why was it open, Eleanor? It's always been locked before. And *who* called you? What force was so strong that it almost drew you to your death? Suppose the upper door had been loose? (*Pause. Eleanor looks at the floor.*) You don't have to tell us . . . perhaps you can't. But tomorrow you must go home. I should have sent you away long before now. I've felt this coming.

ELEANOR. (*With a startled cry.*) No! I can't. (*Pleading.*) This is where I belong, now. I *want* to stay . . .

DR. MONTAGUE. That's *just* why you must go. Do you understand me? (*He speaks carefully and precisely.*) I only hope it isn't too late, already. Too late for you . . . (*He glances at the others.*) too late for all of us. (*Eleanor lowers her head into her hands as the others stand about her in a semi-circle, looking at her wordlessly, and*)

THE CURTAIN FALLS

ACT THREE

SCENE TWO

The following morning. As the curtain rises only the parlor is illuminated. Dr. Montague is at the desk, U. L., working on his notes, while Mrs. Montague and Arthur sit on the sofa culling through the sheaf of papers resulting from their planchette sessions. Luke lounges in one of the D. L. chairs, engrossed in a book. The U. C. doors open, and Mrs. Dudley appears.

MRS. DUDLEY. (*To Dr. Montague.*) She's all packed. She said I was to tell you.

DR. MONTAGUE. (*Glancing up from his work.*) Thank you,

69

Mrs. Dudley. Mr. Sanderson has offered to help with the luggage. (*Luke looks up from his book.*)

MRS. DUDLEY. Just as well. Too heavy for me. Anyway, I don't wait on people. (*Luke smiles.*)

DR. MONTAGUE. (*Long suffering.*) I know, Mrs. Dudley. It's not what you agreed to do.

MRS. DUDLEY. (*Coldly.*) Will that be all?

DR. MONTAGUE. Yes, thank you. (*She closes the doors and is gone. Dr. Montague turns in his chair to speak to Luke.*) Would you mind terribly, my boy?

LUKE. (*Getting up.*) Arthur and I have things all worked out, right Arthur? I attend to the bags and he'll bring the car around. (*To Arthur.*) Shall we?

ARTHUR. Righto. (*To Mrs. Montague.*) I got as far as Merrigot's message about Aunt Beatrice. I'll put a paper clip where I stopped. (*Mrs. Montague nods. Arthur gets up and starts to cross u.*)

LUKE. You know which car?

ARTHUR. (*Slightly indignant.*) Of course. (*He pulls a key from his pocket.*) Got the key after breakfast. Have to be organized. Tell my fellows that. (*He crosses u. c. and exits.*)

LUKE. (*Going out after him. Mumbling.*) Mark of a man, I'm sure. (*He winks at Dr. Montague. Dr. Montague begins putting his notes in his briefcase. Mrs. Montague speaks to him over the back of the sofa.*)

MRS. MONTAGUE. I really don't know why you're being so secretive about your notes, John. I've always been more than willing to share my findings with you. Despite your patronizing attitude.

DR. MONTAGUE. You have your methods, I have mine. I see no reason to confuse matters by arguing over whose approach is correct.

MRS. MONTAGUE. (*Reasonably.*) My theory was that in comparing notes it might be possible to gain a broader range of understanding. I wouldn't think you'd object to that.

DR. MONTAGUE. I don't . . . in principle.

MRS. MONTAGUE. But you place more confidence in what happens to that neurotic girl than in planchette? Is that it?

DR. MONTAGUE. In a sense. And I don't think that "neurotic" is quite the accurate term. There are dangerous forces at work here in Hill House, forces quite alien to your love-starved, benevolent spirits.

MRS. MONTAGUE. Oh, pooh. For a man of science you really amaze me at times.

DR. MONTAGUE. Well, try to contain yourself. (*He snaps the briefcase shut.*) When my book is finished I'll give you an advance copy—and then you can debate my findings as much as you choose. In the meantime I must do as I think best. And getting Eleanor away from here is the first item of business. (*He rises.*)

MRS. MONTAGUE. Really, John, you are exasperating. (*The* u. c. *doors open and Eleanor and Theodora enter, followed by Luke. Dr. Montague crosses to Eleanor and takes her hands.*)

DR. MONTAGUE. Ah, my dear. We hate to see you go. But you'll thank us in time. Arthur is bringing your car around now.

ELEANOR. (*Looking perplexed.*) I don't know what to say.

DR. MONTAGUE. (*Gently.*) It's all decided. You've been here quite long enough.

THEODORA. He's right, Nell. You've got to get away from here.

ELEANOR. (*Uncertainly.*) But . . .

LUKE. (*Somberly.*) Madam, you are no longer welcome as my guest.

MRS. MONTAGUE. Perhaps Arthur should drive her back to the city. He could see that she gets there safely. (*She rises.*)

ELEANOR. Gets where? (*She turns to Mrs. Montague.*) Gets where?

DR. MONTAGUE. Why, home, of course.

THEODORA. Your little place, Nell. Your own apartment. Where all your things are.

ELEANOR. (*A bitter laugh.*) Apartment! I haven't any apartment. I made it up. I sleep on a cot at my sister's, in the baby's room. I haven't any home, no place at all. (*She laughs again.*) And I can't go back to my sister's, because I stole her car to get here. (*She crosses D.*)

THEODORA. (*Sympathetically.*) Nell . . .

ELEANOR. (*Turning to the others.*) It's true. Everything in all the world that belongs to me is in a carton in the back of the car. Some books, some things I had when I was a little girl, and a watch my mother gave me. (*She shakes her head slowly.*) So you see . . . There's no place you can send me. (*The others look at her*

71

in silence. She smiles.) Anyway . . . I want to stay here. (*She sits on the sofa.*)

MRS. MONTAGUE. (*Matter-of-factly.*) I had Arthur call her sister. I must say, she asked first about the car. A rather vulgar person, I gather. (*To her husband.*) But I do think, John, that you were very wrong to let her steal her sister's car and come here.

DR. MONTAGUE. (*Helplessly.*) My dear . . .

MRS. MONTAGUE. At any rate she *is* expected. The sister was most annoyed; seemed they had planned to go off on their own vacation. I *still* think someone ought to see her safely into their hands.

DR. MONTAGUE. (*Firmly.*) It would be a mistake, believe me. She must be allowed to forget everything about Hill House as quickly and as completely as possible—and by herself. Once away from here, she will be all right again. (*He crosses to Eleanor.*) Can you find your way home?

ELEANOR. (*After looking at him in silence for a moment. Quietly.*) The house wants me to stay . . . (*His face clouds.*) I'm sorry . . . really I am.

DR. MONTAGUE. (*Levelly.*) You'll go to Hillsdale, then turn east on Route Five. At Ashton you join Route Thirty-nine, and that will take you home. (*Pause.*) It's for your own good, believe me.

ELEANOR. (*Shaking her head.*) I'm really terribly sorry.

DR. MONTAGUE. (*Unyielding.*) We can't take any more chances, do you understand? I realize now what a terrible risk I have been asking of you all. Now, do you remember the directions?

ELEANOR. Look . . . I wasn't afraid. I really *wasn't* afraid. I was—happy. (*She looks at Dr. Montague earnestly.*) *Happy.* I don't want to go away from here.

DR. MONTAGUE. (*Sternly.*) I won't be responsible for what might happen next. That's final. (*He helps her to her feet.*) You'll forget all this very soon, I promise you.

ELEANOR. (*Dazedly, as she gets up.*) How long have we been here?

THEODORA. Almost a week. Why?

ELEANOR. It's the only time anything's ever really happened to me. I liked it.

DR. MONTAGUE. That is exactly why you are leaving in such a hurry. The decision is no longer yours. (*He urges her u.*)

ELEANOR. (*Resisting.*) I won't go away.

DR. MONTAGUE. You *will* go away. Right now. (*He again tries to draw her u. Arthur enters u. c. and watches quietly. Eleanor reaches her hand out to Luke. Dr. Montague relents for a moment.*)

ELEANOR. Luke, thank you for bringing me down last night. That was wrong of me. I know it now, and you were very brave.

LUKE. I was indeed. (*He smiles.*) But I'm glad to see you going, Nell, because I don't think I could ever do it again. (*He holds her hand silently.*)

MRS. MONTAGUE. (*Breaking the mood.*) Well, it seems to me if you're going you'd best get on with it. We've got better things to do than stand here arguing, when we all know you've got to go. Anyway, it's quite a trip back to the city—and your sister's waiting to go on her vacation.

ARTHUR. Just say goodbye and go. That's the best way. Don't hold with tearful farewells.

MRS. MONTAGUE. (*Turning to Dr. Montague.*) Arthur would be glad . . .

DR. MONTAGUE. (*Decisively.*) No. Eleanor has to go back the way she came—alone. (*Mrs. Montague shrugs impatiently.*)

ELEANOR. (*Half-serious.*) And who do I thank for a lovely time? (*Dr. Montague takes Eleanor by the arm again and steers her to the u. c. doors. Eleanor holds back.*) Doctor . . . please, Doctor.

DR. MONTAGUE. (*Firmly.*) I'm sorry.

LUKE. Drive carefully, Nell.

ELEANOR. (*At the u. c. doors. To Dr. Montague.*) You can't just make me go. You *brought* me here.

DR. MONTAGUE. And I am sending you away. (*Eleanor looks at him defiantly for a moment, and then capitulates. Dr. Montague opens the doors, and motions her to exit. She takes a step into the doorway.*)

MRS. MONTAGUE. Goodbye.

ARTHUR. Have a good trip. (*Eleanor stops and turns to them, smiling wanly. She reaches her hand out to Theodora.*)

ELEANOR. Theo?

THEODORA. (*Crossing to her quickly.*) I thought you weren't going to say goodbye to me. (*She seizes Eleanor's hand.*) Nell? *Please* be happy. Someday things really *will* be all right again, and we'll write letters and visit each other and have fun talking over

73

the crazy things that went on in Hill House. (*She smiles.*) Come on, now. We'll go with you to your car.

ELEANOR. (*Withdrawing her hand.*) Goodbye. (*She turns to the others.*) Goodbye, Mrs. Montague, Arthur. Goodbye, Doctor. I hope your book is very successful. Luke—goodbye. (*Luke nods and smiles warmly.*)

THEODORA. Nell—please take care.

ELEANOR. (*Not looking at her.*) Goodbye. (*She turns and goes out* U. C. *Dr. Montague exits after her, and then the others follow. The* U. C. *doors remain open. After a pause, from off* L., *comes the sound of a car door closing. Then Eleanor's voice is heard through an overhead speaker.*)

ELEANOR'S VOICE. (*Quietly.*) They will watch me down the drive as far as they can see, until I am out of sight and they think I'm really gone. But I *won't* go. Hill House is not as easy as *they* are. Just by telling me to go away they can't make me leave, not if Hill House means me to stay. (*She laughs.*) "Go away, Eleanor, we don't want you any more, not in *our* Hill House, you can't stay here." But I can, I *can*. They don't make the rules around here. I won't go . . . I belong here in Hill House . . . in Hill House . . . (*Her voice fades out. The sound of a car starting and driving off is heard. Then Dr. Montague's voice.*)

DR. MONTAGUE'S VOICE. (*Also through the speaker.*) It may seem incomprehensible to you now, but a place like this . . . sometimes it can begin to affect you without your really being aware. I don't mean the things that occur outwardly, but rather what might happen to you inwardly, as it were. You must promise to tell me immediately if you feel the house catching at you . . . catching at you . . . (*His voice fades out.*)

ELEANOR'S VOICE. (*Filled with nervous excitement.*) They can't run fast enough to stop me . . . not this time. I wonder who will notice first? (*She laughs.*) I'm really doing it . . . all by myself . . . I really am. Now, at last, this is me. (*Pause. Then, tense and frightened.*) But why? *Why* am I doing this? *Why?* Won't somebody stop me? Somebody . . . help . . . me? (*There is a distant crash, off* L., *and then the sound of screams and cries:* "Eleanor!" "Good lord, she hit the tree!" "Quickly, my boy." *Silence, and then the low roar of wind in the hallway,* U. C. *The lights begin to fade, gradually modulating to a spotlight which holds on the* U. C.

74

doors. Slowly but steadily the doors close with a final click, and the strange, disembodied laugh is heard from the speaker. It is repeated several times, growing softer and more distant, and then the spotlight on the doors narrows to darkness, and)

THE CURTAIN FALLS

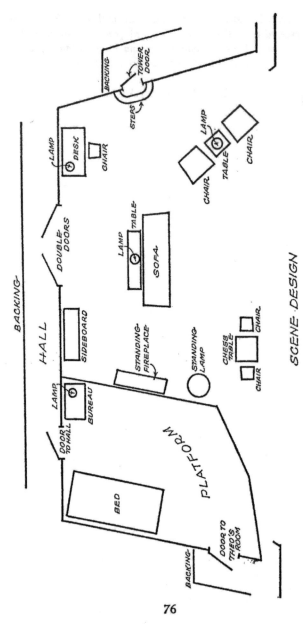

SCENE DESIGN

"THE HAUNTING OF HILL HOUSE"

PROPERTY PLOT

On Stage—All Acts

Parlor area:
  Standing lamp
  Standing fireplace
  Sideboard, on it:
    Decanters (2)
    Tray
    Wine glasses (4)
  Desk, with chair
  Lamp, on desk
  Chess table and set, with chairs (2)
  Sofa
  Long table, with lamp, behind sofa
  Large chairs (2)
  Table, with lamp, between chairs

Bedroom area:
  Single bed
  Bureau, with lamp
(All furniture, in both areas, should be of ornate, massive mid-Victorian style)

ACT ONE—*Scene 1*
  Book, on table between chairs—On Stage

ACT ONE—*Scene 2*
  Suitcase, filled, on bed—On Stage
  Flask (Luke)—Off R.

ACT TWO—*Scene 1*
  Book (Eleanor) ⎫
  Coffee cup and saucer ⎬ On Stage
  Large scrapbook, on desk ⎭
  Slip of paper (Luke) ⎫ Personal
  Flashlight (Dr. Montague) ⎭

ACT TWO—*Scene 2*
  Book (Eleanor) ⎫ On Stage
  Large scrapbook (Theodora) ⎭
  Sheaf of papers (Arthur)—Off C.

Act Three—*Scene 1*
  Sheaf of notes (Theodora) } Off c.
  Flashlight (Dr. Montague) }
  Revolver (Arthur)

Act Three—*Scene 2*
  Briefcase, notes and pen, on desk
  Sheaf of papers (Arthur and Mrs. Montague) } On Stage
  Book (Luke)
  Car keys and paper clip (Arthur)—
    Personal